Introducing Artificial Intelligence

G L Simons

PUBLISHED BY NCC PUBLICATIONS

British Library Cataloguing in Publication Data

Simons, G. L.
Introducing artificial intelligence
1. Artificial intelligence
I. Title
001.53'5   Q335

ISBN 0-85012-457-3

First published in 1984 by:

NCC Publications, The National Computing Centre Ltd, Oxford Road, Manchester M1 7ED, England.

Typeset in 11pt Times Roman and printed in England by UPS Blackburn Limited, 76-80 Northgate, Blackburn, Lancashire.

ISBN 0-85012-457-3 (NCC Publications)

ISBN 0-470-201-665 (Halsted Press)

Introduction

This is an introductory book aimed at a wide cross-section of non-technical readers. It has three main purposes:

1) to set artificial intelligence (AI) in a broad context of historical attitudes, imaginative insights, and ideas about intelligence in general;

2) to acquaint readers with the principal topics of interest to AI researchers (there is a wide range of disciplines and studies that relate to work in AI);

3) to indicate, with some examples, that AI is no longer solely an esoteric laboratory pursuit, but increasingly a commercial matter (AI-related products are available in the marketplace for many different purposes).

There is nothing in this publication about how to write AI programs. Such programs are frequently mentioned but no examples of coding are given, and no attempt is made to indicate the main features of the growing spectrum of AI languages. Readers requiring more detailed information are referred to the list of references (Appendix 1) and to the items in the Select Bibliography (Appendix 2).

This book aims to give a flavour of what is happening in an increasingly important field that links computer science, psychology, commerce, industry and other social sectors. It provides an insight into a rapidly expanding field that will have wide-ranging consequences for society in the years ahead.

Contents

PART 2   OBJECTIVES AND METHODS

Part 1

BACKGROUND

1 The Nature of Intelligence

INTRODUCTION

This book is largely concerned with efforts to build intelligence into machines. Such efforts would seem to presuppose that we have a clear concept of *natural* intelligence, of the mental and behavioural abilities that can be found in human beings and perhaps also in other animals. In fact, our view of natural intelligence is constantly shifting, mediated not only by new biological knowledge but also by the emerging competence of artificial systems. It is useful to glance at attitudes to intelligence that mostly predate computer progress over the last three or four decades. In this way we can see that the concept of intelligence has many dimensions, not all of which may be relevant to the design and manufacture of clever machines. (And we may also expect a reciprocal effect: progress in designing artificial intelligence will increasingly throw light on what it means to belong to an intelligent biological species.)

In everyday usage 'intelligence' and its derivatives are familiar words: it is rarely thought ambiguous to declare that this or that person is intelligent, or that intelligence is a desirable human characteristic. But when we try to define 'intelligence' we may find that the concept becomes elusive. Is it concerned with the manipulation of numbers, words or other symbols? Is it related to practical action in the world? Does it bear on creativity and invention? Do we find intelligence in mental activity or in effective behaviour? And how is intelligence related to such phenomena as willing, learning, remembering and emotion? We are finding it possible to build a degree of intelligence into *artefacts* without understanding fully the nature of *natural* intelligence. But awareness of views about intelligence in human beings can indicate what may or may not be possible for machines.

WHAT IS INTELLIGENCE?

On Definitions

Definitions – of anything – aspire to completeness. The definition that leaves out some important feature of an entity is rightly regarded as inadequate. And where the topic is complex or nebulous, as *intelligence* can be, definitions are particularly at risk. Can we define intelligence? Should we even try? Perhaps it is better simply to list appropriate mental and behavioural activities to convey an impression of intelligence.

There are in fact various *types* of definitions that should not be confused. Miles (1957), for example, identified:

—   *real definitions*, concerned with the actual entities to which the terms refer;

—   *nominal definitions*, concerned with the meanings of words rather than the entities that the words are supposed to denote. Here *lexical* definitions focus on how words are commonly used; *stipulative* definitions focus on how a person intends to use a term;

—   *operational definitions*, concerned with meanings in terms of observable, measurable operations.

To these types of definition we may add *definition by enumeration*, where the nature of an entity or word is described by listing characteristic features. This approach can reveal that there are many different types of the entity in question, and help to avoid the confusion that arises when different people use a word correctly but with different meanings. Confusion of this sort can beset discussion of *intelligence*.

Types of Intelligence

We commonly imagine intelligence to consist in such things as the ability to solve problems, do sums, learn, cope with new situations, etc. It is assumed that people in responsible positions – managers, doctors, cabinet ministers, etc – are intelligent, an assumption that sometimes leads us into paradox: 'if so and so is so intelligent why does he/she act/talk so foolishly?' This encourages us to identify different *kinds* of intelligence. The brilliant mathematician may have no political insight, and a first-class degree in Greats says nothing about the individual's capacity to act intelligently in human relationships.

To some extent the different types of intelligence are recognised in language. Thus we may talk of judgement, wisdom, insight, perception and learning. Intelligence may be 'manipulative', 'verbal', 'philosophical', etc. We will see that such distinctions are important to an understanding of *artificial* intelligence: computers may be seen as highly skilled at mathematics, much less competent at tasks requiring what we would call judgement or wisdom. At the same time we should not be trapped in rigid categories. Biological intelligence has evolved over millions of years, and the infant enlarges its spectrum of intelligence as it grows to maturity: in analogous fashion there is a discernible evolution of *computer* intelligence.

Sometimes a distinction is made between *intelligence* and specific intellectual *abilities*, where intelligence is seen as the capacity to acquire particular skills rather than the skills themselves. Thus someone who takes a month to master simple differential equations may be deemed less intelligent than someone who needs only a few minutes. A skill may be acquired through laborious effort over a lengthy period, and its presence may indicate at least a certain minimal intelligence (some skills cannot be taught to some people).

It has also been suggested that the capacity to acquire intellectual skills is a *general* capacity, equally relevant to skills of different types. One of the criticisms of artificial intelligence is that individual AI programs tend to focus on specific isolated tasks (game-playing, theorem-proving, story-writing, etc) and so lack the generality that characterises real intelligence. (We will see that this is not a particularly telling criticism: a computer can easily be given access to different AI programs to extend its range of competence, and moreover there are already AI programs that embody the requisite general capacity, eg the General Problem Solver of Ernst and Newell – see Chapters 4 and 8.)

Some observers have been tempted to *reify* intelligence, much in the way that certain mental attributes can be wrongly represented as *soul* or *spirit*. In fact intelligence should be regarded as an abstraction from certain kinds of behaviour. It is only through behaviour that we can recognise intelligence, even though the behaviour may then allow us to deduce mental (or even, some would say, metaphysical) capacities. This approach is important to an evaluation of intelligence in computer systems: a computer-based system will be deemed intelligent by virtue of *what it can do*, ie how it behaves with regard to problem-solving, decision-making, inference drawing, etc.

Pyle (1979) has emphasised that 'intelligence' is a 'situation-specific' word. It can be seen to take on different meanings according to the particular situation. We have noted that it can signify the capacity to *acquire* a skill, but it can also indicate particular abilities in particular circumstances, eg driving a car, writing a poem, solving a crossword puzzle (Dockrell, 1970). But a capacity to *acquire* a skill implies a *potential* for behaving in certain ways. In saying that a person is intelligent we are, at least in part, imagining how the person *would* behave in circumstances that may not yet have occurred. And we can observe that this idea connects well with what some people see as the *general* capacity of intelligence: a full description of *current* performance does not exhaust the possibilities of the intelligent system.

The various definitions and descriptions of intelligence highlight, to some extent, the interests of individual researchers. Pyle (p 3) lists a few important researchers and their definitions, and notes that most say something about the ability to reason:

Binet: to judge well, to comprehend well, to reason well.

Spearman: general intelligence . . . involves mainly the 'education of relations and correlates'.

Terman: the capacity to form concepts and to grasp their significance.

Vernon: 'all-round thinking capacity' or 'mental efficiency'.

Burt: innate, general, cognitive ability.

Heim: intelligent activity consists in grasping the essentials in a situation and responding appropriately to them.

Wechsler: the aggregate or global capacity of the individual to act purposefully, to think rationally and to deal effectively with the environment.

Piaget: adaptation to the physical and social environment.

The mix of abilities (judgement, comprehension, reasoning, concept-formation, appropriate response, adaptation, etc) in these definitions highlights the multifaceted nature of intelligence. No single definition exhausts the possibilities. A system – biological or artificial – with only one skill or capacity has very limited intelligence, if the system is intelligent at all.

It is inevitable that workers in artificial intelligence would need to scrutinise natural intelligence to identify key characteristics, definitive attributes, etc. You cannot begin to frame intelligence in artefacts until you have some concepts about how intelligence is to be recognised in biological systems. Douglas Hofstadter, for example, who carries out AI work at Indiana University, has indicated what he regards as 'essential abilities for intelligence'. These include the capacity to respond to situations flexibly, to exploit fortuitous circumstances, to make sense out of ambiguous or contradictory messages, to find similarities in situations separated by differences, and to generate new concepts and novel ideas. Again the multifaceted character of intelligence is evident.

The Hofstadter 'essential abilities' emphasise such aspects as judgement, insight and creativity, elements which are not normally associated with computers. Indeed the conventional wisdom would have it that computers are inflexible and unimaginative, preoccupied with blind obedience to rules, as incapable of independent initiative as a train on a track. But researchers in artificial intelligence have a different view. Hence Hofstadter (1979) remarks: '. . . the strange flavour of AI work is that people try to put together long sets of rules in strict formalisms which tell inflexible machines how to be flexible.'

The multidimensional nature of intelligence suggests that some elements of intelligence will more easily be structured into artificial systems than others. It is, for example, much easier to quantify and measure computational intelligence than to quantify and measure such elements as judgement or creativity. And unless an element can be quantified, in some sense, it is difficult to see how it could be encapsulated in a computer program. Developments in computer science have encouraged a cognitive approach to human psychology, including human intelligence. This psychological approach has in turn stimulated ideas on how human mental processes can be modelled in computer systems.

The Cognitive Approach

The *cognitive model* of the human mind is based on the idea of information processing. It is assumed that every human being is equipped with the same basic information processing system, and that all mental processes can in principle be explained in terms of the operation of this system. The principal components of the information processing system are shown in Figure 1.1

Information from the outside world impinges on the sense receptors (these receptors can rely on changes in natural phenomena, such as air pressure, temperature, distribution of molecules, and electromagnetic radiation). At first the information is held in a *short-term sensory store* (sometimes called a 'sensory buffer'). This store has a large capacity and theoretically can hold all the information presented to the sensory receptors – but for a very short time only (for example, for 0.5 second for

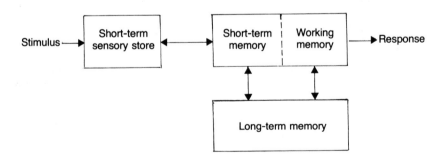

Figure 1.1   Information Processing Model of Human Mind

visual information). It is possible that there is a short-term sensory store for each sense.

According to the immediate needs of the individual, attention may or may not be paid to the information briefly held in the short-term sensory store: in normal experience, vast quantities of information fade without being noticed by the individual. In the cases where attention *is* paid to the short-term sensory store, it is likely that some of the information will be transferred to the *short-term memory*. In this (conscious) memory, a few items can be held for up to about 0.25 minute unless 'pushed out' by other incoming items. An effort can be made to keep information active in consciousness (this effort is sometimes called 'rehearsal'). The short-term memory has a much smaller capacity than the sensory buffer but *chunking techniques* can be used to cluster information, and so increase the spectrum of current awareness.

The *working memory* is sometimes regarded as an appendage to short-term memory and as having limited capacity and intermediate-term storage capabilities. Working memory functions as a mental scratch pad on which conscious intellectual tasks can be performed. As with short-term memory, information is quickly lost from working memory unless a rehearsal strategy is adopted.

Information can be transferred from short-term memory to *long-term memory*. Vast amounts of information can be held in long-term memory and there is little or no fading with time. Sometimes retrieval paths are blocked, for one reason or another, and information items are effectively lost until the blocks can be removed. In the absence of preventive blocks, *search strategies* are employed for item-retrieval purposes.

If these storage and operational elements characterise all human beings, we would still expect considerable variation from one individual to another. One person can remember more than another and may be better at searching long-term memory. Such operations as chunking, paying attention and encoding information (for transfer from short-term to long-term memory) vary in efficiency from one individual to another – and such variations indicate how intelligence can vary throughout a population.

The various types of intelligence can be explored within the framework of the information processing model. Consider, for example, the verbal intelligence required for reading. It has been pointed out (eg by Hunt, Lunneborg and Lewis, 1975) that there are around 500,000 morphemes (linguistic units – words or parts of words – that have meaning) in the typical novel. Reading involves looking up in memory each morpheme, as it is visually encountered, to ascertain its meaning. It is obvious that even a small difference in search time, from one individual to another, is very significant when it is multiplied by the number of morphemes in a piece of text. Similarly, the holding capacity of a person's short-term memory will in part determine the ease with which a text is read: a person who can hold many words at once, without mixing up the order, should find reading easier than if only a few words could be carried in short-term memory.

Hence reading speed, a commonly-accepted index to one type of intelligence, can be usefully explored within the terms suggested by the cognitive approach. The same can be said, *mutatis mutandis*, for other types of intelligence.

The cognitive approach is important to artificial intelligence since it provides a model that is characteristic of existing computer systems. This is not coincidental. Progress in computer science has been the key factor encouraging researchers to develop an information-processing model for psychological phenomena. Thus it is clear that the success of cognitive interpretations of human psychology will to a large extent define the scope of artificial intelligence. If, for example, we can give an information-processing explanation of emotion it may be possible to structure emotion into artificial systems. We are already building systems that can learn, remember and reason. It may not be too fanciful to suggest that in the relatively near future we will be able to construct artefacts that are capable of imagination, intuition and emotional sensitivity.

INTELLIGENCE IN HISTORY

There has always been interest in the mind and related phenomena, though the terminology and the focus have varied throughout history. Plato recognised three broad types of mental attributes (intellectual, emotional and moral) which modern psychologists would recognise as cognition, affection and cona-tion. In a much quoted passage in the *Phaedrus*, he compares the intellect to a charioteer who holds the reins, and the emotional and moral faculties to a pair of horses that draw the vehicle. Aristotle preferred a twofold characterisation: for him there are the 'dian-oetic' (cognitive or intellectual) capacities of the mind and the 'orectic' (emotional and moral). Cicero, influenced by Greek philosophy, coined the word *intellegentia* to denote the intellectual faculty.

There was little specific focus on intelligence per se until modern times. Terminology and interests shifted through the Middle Ages, and intelligence was rarely considered in the writings of those who led the scientific revolution in the seventeenth and eighteenth centuries (such philosophers as Descartes, Locke and Hume). Up to the middle of the nineteenth century, psychologists were mostly interested in knowledge, experience, character and will – topics that do not encapsulate what is meant by intelligence today. How-ever, the work of Herbert Spencer (eg *Principles of Psychology*, 1870) uses the term 'intelligence' to denote a fundamental capac-ity of cognition, one that 'progressively differentiates into a hierar-chy of more specialised abilities' (sensory, perceptual, associative, etc). At this time, some of the first attempts were being made to research individual differences that were seen to be relevant to intelligence. For example, Galton (1883) explored the speed of response to flashing lights, and Ebbinghaus (1897) investigated the capacity to learn nonsense syllables. Such experiments contri-buted little to an understanding of intelligence. It was found, for instance, that the results bore little relationship to students' work, and individuals could be good on one test and poor on another. However, the scene was set for the more useful measurement approach to intelligence that was to develop in the twentieth century (see below).

Sir Cyril Burt has described how *intelligence* became an impor-tant scientific concept and how the word became common in popular usage. He pointed out that even in his own boyhood the word was rarely used, and that he never heard either teachers or parents talk of a child's 'intelligence'. After Spencer and Galton reintroduced the concept in the nineteenth century, the term came into general use much later. Neurologists (such as Jackson and Sherrington) and other psychologists with a physiological training accepted the idea of a general cognitive capacity probably related to the complexity of neuron connections in the cerebral cortex. Burt (1955) came to regard intelligence as:

> . . . a mental trait of fundamental importance defined by three verifiable attributes: first, it is a general quality . . . secondly, it is an intellectual quality . . . thirdly, it is inherited or at least innate . . . We thus arrive at the concept of an innate, general, cognitive ability.

It is certainly possible to dispute this description but it does highlight some of the elements regarded by modern psychologists as important to the concept of intelligence.

MEASURING INTELLIGENCE

Early Efforts

It is useful from an AI point of view to be able to measure natural intelligence. Where intelligence is maintained as a nebulous or metaphysical commodity it cannot be modelled in a computer system. Attempts to measure (ie to quantify) intelligence have prepared the way for its effective encapsulation in artificial systems. Such attempts have been made for more than a century.

Efforts to measure intelligence began with the work of Sir Francis Galton. Friend of Herbert Spencer and cousin of Charles Darwin, he was influenced by them both. In his study of pedigree, *Hereditary Genius* (1869), Galton tried to prove that mental attributes were inherited 'pre-formed', with variation from one individual to another. He was conscious of the growing interest in the possibility of measuring mental attributes.

Galton argued that since intelligence had a physical basis, it must be graded – as are such physical attributes as height and weight – throughout a population. At Galton's suggestion, the mathematician Karl Pearson developed a measure of association between variables, an index of correlation termed the *product-moment coefficient* (also known as the correlation coefficient). This measure, together with other factor-analysis techniques, allows many variables to be investigated.

The first tests of mental ability were carried out by Galton in his 'anthropometric laboratory', and by J. McK. Cattell in America. Efforts were made to test such things as reaction times, visual and auditory acuity, sensitivity to pain, memory and mental imagery. Miller (1964) gives a list of the tests proposed by Cattell (1890) to measure intelligence:

Dynamometer pressure. How tightly can the hand squeeze?

Rate of movement. How quickly can the hand be moved through a distance of 50 cm?

Sensation-areas. How far apart must two points be on the skin to be recognised as two rather than one?

Pressure causing pain. How much pressure on the forehead is necessary to cause pain?

Least noticeable difference in weight. How large must the difference be between two weights before it is reliably detected?

Reaction time for sound. How quickly can the hand be moved at the onset of an auditory signal?

Time for naming colours. How long does it take to name a strip of ten coloured papers?

Bisection of 50-cm. line. How accurately can one point to the centre of an ebony rule?

Judgement of 10-sec. time. How accurately can an interval of 10 seconds be judged?

Number of letters remembered on once hearing. How many letters, ordered at random, can be repeated exactly after one presentation?

We need not be surprised that such measures revealed differences among people. However, it was found impossible to correlate such differences with variations in other fields, such as educational achievement or social standing. Galton rejected the correlations because, with this approach, Britain's ruling families were found to have an 'intelligence' no greater than that of common labourers.

Charles Spearman, following the Galton/Pearson initiatives, tested children for various mental abilities (memory, reasoning, etc) at the beginning of the twentieth century. He found that the tests were positively correlated, ie if the children scored well on one test they would tend to score well on others. This suggested a factor (termed 'g' for 'general intelligence') which was common to all the tests. But at the same time, all the tests did not produce identical results, so each was associated with a smaller specific ability. Spearman called these smaller factors 'Ss' or 'specific abilities'. Thus was born the *two-factor model* of intelligence. In contrast, later researchers found many primary mental abilities that were worthy of measurement. Thurstone, for instance, reckoned that all tests of mental ability could be grouped into seven categories: verbal comprehension, number, memory, perceptual speed, space, verbal fluency, and inductive reasoning. More ambitiously, Guilford designed a system for specifying no less than 120 separate mental abilities. The scheme was based, not on factor analysis, but on a logical exploration of the elements involved in mental activity. These different approaches highlight the problems involved in trying to identify the key elements in intelligence.

Binet to Wechsler

In 1904 a commission was appointed in France by the Minister for Public Instruction to study how retarded children could best be taught. The resulting recommendations required that a reliable means be found of identifying retarded children. Alfred Binet, one of the commission members, and his co-worker Simon produced a scale designed to solve this problem. It contained thirty items arranged in ascending order of difficulty, including such tasks as:

— imitating gestures and following simple commands;

— naming objects in pictures;

— drawing designs from memory;

— putting three nouns in a sentence;

— defining abstract words.

Such test items, very different to the Galton/Cattell sensory tests, were designed to investigate judgement, comprehension and reasoning. These were qualities seen by Binet as essential elements in intelligence. He then set out to ascertain the mental level of the average child at various ages. When the Binet-Simon Scale was revised, in 1908 and 1911, items were graded to facilitate a calculation of mental age. Stern, in 1912, proposed that the ratio of mental age to chronological age could yield an effective intelligence quotient (IQ). But there were good reasons for doubting the value of this sort of categorisation of children. Binet himself reacted against what he saw as the 'brutal pessimism' enshrined in this type of approach ("Some recent philosophers appear to have given their moral support to the deplorable verdict that the intelligence of an individual is a fixed quantity . . . We must protest and act against this brutal pessimism"). He and Simon did not intend the Scale to be used in such a fashion.

Lewis Terman, at Stanford University, published in 1916 a further revision of the Binet-Simon Scale. Based on the testing of about 1000 children and 400 adults, the new scheme was intended for standardised use in the United States. A later Terman revision of the Scale was published in 1937. However, many psychologists were coming to believe that revisions to the Binet-Simon Scale were misplaced, and that a totally new approach was required. For example, some items in the Terman revised version were of little interest to adults; too few adults had been included in the standardisation procedures; and the concept of mental age was inapplicable. For these reasons, David Wechsler, chief psychologist at New York's Bellevue Psychiatric Hospital, developed the Wechsler-Bellevue Intelligence Scale in 1939 (revised as the Wechsler Adult Intelligence Scale, WAIS, in 1955). The Wechsler Intelligence Scale for Children (WISC) was introduced in 1949 (and revised in 1974). A central Wechsler idea is that of the *deviation IQ*, which indicates in standard deviation units how a person's score relates to the norm for his own age group. Thus if the decline in a person's performance is the same as that of the normative sample, then the person's IQ remains constant.

IQ and AI

The attempts to measure (ie to quantify) *natural* intelligence are relevant to efforts to build *artificial* intelligence. Where biological intelligence is seen as a component of non-physical minds it is difficult to imagine how intelligence could ever be structured in electronic circuits. Today, however, psychology is rarely troubled by metaphysical assumptions: researchers generally believe that intelligence is a property of certain types of physical systems, thus allowing the possibility that intelligent systems can be designed and built by human beings. At the same time, there is still anxiety that attitudes to the measurement of intelligence have both adversely affected attitudes to human potential and raised false expectations about the scope of intelligence in artificial systems. Joseph Weizenbaum, the celebrated Professor of Computer Science at the Massachusetts Institute of Technology, is often associated with this sort of anxiety.

Weizenbaum (1976) declares that:

> Few "scientific" concepts have so thoroughly muddled the thinking of both scientists and the general public as that of the "intelligence quotient" or "I.Q." The idea that intelligence can be quantitatively measured along a simple linear scale has caused untold harm to our society in general, and to education in particular.

It is suggested, in a spirit reminiscent of Binet, that it is misleading to regard intelligence as an unalterable attribute of individuals (like the colour of their eyes) and to suggest that it may even be genetically transmittable from one generation to the next. Moreover IQ testing, it is argued, is indifferent to how human creativity depends not only on intellect 'but also crucially on an interplay between intellect and other modalities of thought, such as intuition and wisdom . . .' And it is necessary to define the context, the frame of reference, in which any exploration of intelligence is to take place.

It follows, according to Weizenbaum, that intelligence can only be understood in specific social and cultural contexts, and that it is misleading to compare different types of intelligence. Hence it is seen as sterile to discuss whether computers 'more intelligent than man' will ever be built. Weizenbaum had hoped to discover a proof that there was an upper limit on how much intelligence a machine could achieve, much in the way that Claud Shannon had demonstrated an upper bound on the amount of information that an information channel could transmit. But Weizenbaum's own approach prohibited the possibility of an 'upper-bound proof' in the case of intelligence: if intelligence could not be quantified, there could be no upper limit in the Shannon sense. Weizenbaum seems to hope that machine intelligence will be limited but is forced to admit, in his terms, that there is no way of giving such a limit precise meaning or of proving it. But it is difficult to sustain Weizenbaum's general position.

Already it is evident that artificial systems can engage in certain types of intelligent activity that can be graded according to performance. Chess-playing is one of the most obvious examples. Specific computer programs can be compared, on a numerical scale, with any human chess expert. This situation fulfils the requirement that the cultural framework, the domain of the activity, be well defined. But when this is done it seems perfectly reasonable to compare human and machine intelligence: there is no problem, for instance, in assigning both human beings and computer programs particular ratings on the table approved by the US Chess Federation. Once this point is conceded, the debate then shifts. It becomes pertinent to enquire precisely which intelligent-activity domains can be defined to allow licit comparisons between human and machine performance.

One approach, in a limited domain, is to program computers to tackle traditional IQ tests. Mason (1982) explores how a computer may be programmed to find the next term in a numerical sequence. The scale of the problem is obvious when it is realised that there is a 'virtual infinity of relationships which can exist between successive terms of a sequence'. In fact the task can be handled using the calculus of finite differences. A program is shown, written in Microsoft Basic for use with the Video-Genie computer.

It is true that IQ tests are limited to a few types of abilities and that many aspects of human competence are not amenable to testing in this way. However, it does not follow that computers are necessarily incompetent in such areas. Their competence, where it exists, can be evaluated much as it would be for any other behaving system. If a computer system can write poetry or music, translate from one language to another, recognise shapes, adapt to changing circumstances, hold a conversation, etc, then there is no obvious difficulty in assessing its performance in such activities. The type of assessment will depend upon the task, but the domains are clear and well defined.

The task of evaluating machine intelligence in such areas may be technically difficult but it is not philosophically problematic in the sense that we must agonise over whether computers can be called 'intelligent'. Intelligent computers are with us today: the central questions are: *how* intelligent are they? and how intelligent will they *become*? Such questions will only be answered by practical workers in the field. They will not be answered in the context of a general anxiety about the competence of artificial systems.

ASPECTS OF INTELLIGENCE

General

Some aspects of natural intelligence (eg such elements as intuition, judgement and wisdom) are today somewhat less than typical in artificial systems. There is already talk of 'intuitive' programs (see, for example, Surya, 1984) but so far the idea is fanciful. Other elements in natural intelligence can be found in artificial systems. We are accustomed to machines that can remember, compute and initiate actions (behaviours) intended to realise particular objectives. But we may be more surprised to find that existing systems may be said to learn, indulge in creative activity, or manipulate information to synthesise new knowledge.

Here we quickly run into semantic difficulties. What counts as *real* learning behaviour? How do we recognise a genuinely creative act? What are the criteria of new knowledge? People hostile to AI tend to favour definitions that exclude computers from the realm of intelligent behaviour, but the problem is that such definitions tend to exclude also the vast majority of the human race. (It is sometimes pointed out, for example, that man *invented* the game of chess whereas computers merely *learn the rules*. But how many people do *you* know who invented the game of chess?) What we find is that many of the activities associated with intelligent behaviour in human beings can now be found in computer systems.

Learning

It has often been observed that intelligence is closely associated with the capacity to learn. Indeed many IQ tests, perhaps mistakenly, focus on how individuals have retained information about their culture. A person may appear stupid simply because there is a poor learning capacity. It may be difficult for the person to store information about experiences and equally difficult therefore to make intelligent generalisations from such information. We can see that learning is dependent upon effective memory, a key element in both biological and artificial intelligent systems.

Computers are learning how to learn, partly by means of heuristic and adaptive programs that have widely been seen as means whereby machines can learn by experience. Knowledge can be built up, then modified in the light of changing circumstances. G. J. Sussman's HACKER program, for example, can learn general lessons from particular experiences and so improve its performance with practice: mistakes are generalised and added to a file of 'traps' to be avoided. Similarly the celebrated Samuel draughts (checkers) program remembers past successes to improve its current performance.

In one analysis (Gagné 1974, 1977) phases of learning can be identified – these include acquiring information, retention, generalisation, performance and feedback – and also the results of acts of learning (called 'learning outcomes'). Three areas of outcome are acknowledged: knowledge (verbal information, facts, etc); skills (motor and intellectual); and attitudes (towards learning itself and the various cognitive strategies). The General Problem Solver (GPS), perhaps the first of the expert systems, is seen by some as a computerised attempt to become more specific in the analysis of learning outcomes.

Problem Solving

Problem solving (considered in more detail in Chapter 4) ideally depends upon a generalised competence that can affect the outcome of many different kinds of tasks. The use of search strategies is highly relevant to finding solutions to problems, and much AI work is directly concerned with the framing of strategies of this sort. In psychological research, studies to understand problem solving are often associated with investigation of concept attainment. There is the implicit assumption that the formulation of concepts can help the intelligent system to find solutions to problems. Again we can look to GPS as intended to embody a *general* problem-solving capability.

GPS was tested on eleven very different problems – 'missionaries and cannibals', integration, theorem proving, parsing sentences, letter-series completion, etc. The program was able to solve such problems, but not always by producing a goal structure analogous to that used by human beings. Ernst and Newell (1969) saw GPS as yielding 'a series of lessons that yield a more perfect view of the nature of problem solving and what is required to construct processes that accomplish it'.

Today we see a range of techniques studied in psychology, some of which can be programmed for the solution of problems. As we see in other areas, in the field of problem solving there is a reciprocal influence between the investigations of natural intelligence and computer potential.

Creativity

The capacity for creative activity can bear on intelligence in many ways. A creative act is usually, in some sense, unexpected: it represents a break with convention or tradition. It may represent a new solution to a problem, a new insight, a new design, a new conceptual configuration. In short, the creative act is a departure from familiar practice. Creative individuals may be scientists, artists, managers, clowns, politicians, designers, etc: any type of activity can embody the potential for creative development. Computers, like human individuals, can exhibit creative potential when suitably programmed.

We all know that computers can 'paint' pictures, using sophisticated interactive graphics; compose Japanese haiku; generate new melodies and appropriate harmonies. And they can also be creative in the various problem solving domains: creativity, like problem solving, has many facets. Margaret Boden (1977) has suggested that HACKER's learning activity 'is a creative matter', and has indicated how Sussman sees program *bugs* as 'manifestations of powerful strategies of creative thinking' (perhaps, as with human error, pointing to new insights). Hofstadter (1979), after hearing a radio broadcast about computer-generated haiku, reflected upon the implications of making a computer generate 'something which ordinarily would be considered an artistic creation'. He then wrote a flexibly creative computer program, achieving 'strongly surrealistic' results which nevertheless soon bored him because of the restrictions on the program. And there are many examples of where computers have achieved creative solutions to chess problems. For instance, the Chess Champion Mark V system, marketed by SciSys, found three correct solutions to the celebrated Zagorujko chess problem thought to have only one solution.

It is clear that computers can already be creative in various ways, and that such a capability is highly relevant to the question of intelligence in artificial systems. If the capacity for creative acts, of whatever type, is a criterion of intelligence then computer-based systems, appropriately programmed, already qualify.

Behaviour and Biology

Evidence for intelligence must always involve behaviour, even if in the case of computers the behaviour is nothing more than the behaviour of symbols on a screen. With human beings the behaviour may consist in the observable response to a problematic situation, and here the activity may involve the whole body as the individual escapes a predicament, or simply the movement of a hand as a theoretical problem is solved using pen and paper (or a computer keyboard). Sloman (1978) sees intelligent behaviour as being based 'on the ability to cope in a systematic fashion with a range of problems of varying structures, and the ability (consciously or unconsciously) to build, describe, interpret, compare, modify and use complex structures, including symbolic structures like sentences, pictures, maps and plans for action'.

The intimate connection between intelligence and behaviour suggests also links with biology: in the pre-computer world all intelligent behaviour was manifested in biological systems. In fact many psychologists have interpreted intelligence as an adaptive mechanism developed to aid the survival of biological species (for example, this approach is evident in the work of such developmental psychologists as Piaget, Bruner and Vygotsky).

The biological approach to the interpretation of intelligence encourages the closest scrutiny of the working of the brain. This is in accord with the cognitive model of human intelligence (see Figure 1.1). Traditional behaviourist psychology encouraged the view that the brain was a veritable 'black box', with inputs and outputs but with almost irrelevant internal processes. One of the consequences of progress in artificial intelligence is that psychologists have been forced to investigate the internal cognitive structures of the human brain. Allport (1980) has even declared that '. . . the advent of Artificial Intelligence is the single most important development in the history of psychology . . .'.

A consequence of the biological interpretation of intelligence is that artificial systems are not merely being invested with mental characteristics (eg a range of cognitive abilities) but with biological features also. Adaptation may be represented as a survival mechanism in a shifting environment, intelligent adaptation as a feature of sophisticated life-forms. There are implications in this that are rarely addressed.

COGNITION AND CONATION

Most activities in artificial intelligence have a *cognitive* significance, ie they relate to information processing for such purposes as accepting data, remembering, learning, reasoning, problem solving, etc. But we have seen that intelligence can embrace many different types of process or behaviour. Sloman (1978) has emphasised that AI is not solely concerned with 'unusual or meritorious' forms of behaviour: the activities of ordinary human beings and other animals are also of interest. In addition the range of intelligent capabilities covers not only such things as learning, understanding a language, making and testing plans, solving problems, etc, but also having motives, emotions and attitudes.

Researchers in artificial intelligence have devoted little attention to the possibility of building emotion into artificial systems. The *conative* topics of wishing and willing are not mainstream AI research areas at the moment. There is however much talk about computers as intentional systems, having goals and objectives, etc; and emotion is being seriously considered as a possible element in computers (for example, at the universities of Sussex and War-wick). At present the vast bulk of AI work is focusing on cognitive systems (dealing with learning, perception, reasoning, etc). It is possible to frame an information-processing theory of emotion, and in fact traditional psychology does carry many different cognitive hypotheses in this area. But this book, while indicating that no human mental activity is in principle outside the scope of AI, concentrates on what are currently the main areas of AI interest.

SUMMARY

We have seen that there are many types of intelligence, and that different researchers have individually focused on the areas of interest to them. The emergence of artificial intelligence as a branch of computer science has encouraged a view of intelligence as an information-processing phenomenon. This circumstance has reinforced cognitive interpretations of mental activity and indicated how such activity can be modelled in computer systems.

Artificial intelligence today focuses on particular types of activity: learning, reasoning, language understanding, translation, perception, etc (some of these are considered in more detail in Parts II and III). There is interesting speculation on artificial emotion but little if any successful work. There are many types of human intelligence that machines are not even beginning to emulate, but in other areas computer-based systems are undeniably intelligent. It is worth looking at other aspects of the AI background before exploring some of these areas.

2 The AI Background

INTRODUCTION

Artificial intelligence, a new and exciting technology, is not a new concept in human imagination. The idea can be found at least as far back as the pre-Christian Greeks and in all ages thereafter. Homer was acquainted with the concept of AI, perhaps 800 years B.C., and the ancient historian Polybios believed that Nabis, a dictator of Sparta (about 200 B.C.), used a robot to compel rich but recalcitrant citizens to pay their taxes. We tend to think that artificial intelligence is a new idea, hatched in the computer age. In fact it is an ancient notion.

This chapter describes some of the historical and imaginative background to modern AI. Artificial intelligence, as a subclass of computer science, springs from the same soil. The early history of computation, in fact and fiction, is a description also of the genesis of intelligent machines.

It is also necessary to say something about the objections to the idea of AI, the notion that artificial intelligence is somehow an affront to commonsense and humanity. It is sometimes even said that 'artificial intelligence' is a contradiction in terms, the corollary being that intelligence is a unique property of certain types of natural biological systems. But this type of objection is being outflanked by the event. Intelligent machines are already working amongst us. This chapter gives some indication of what they are up to (to be explored in more detail later), and some idea of what we may expect in the future. Any suggested predictions are not given dates, firm or tentative. It is enough that machine competence is developing at a rapid rate.

THE FICTIONAL FRAME

Many technologies are prefigured in fiction. Imaginative ideas are tossed around before finding an embodiment in effective artefacts. Icarus would have been useless in the Battle of Britain but he said something about manned flight. And each age invests in the fictional mode it prefers. In the earliest times, myth was a useful vehicle for aspiring technologists. Perhaps it was the gods who made the first robots.

The Assyro-Babylonian divinity Marduk shaped the body of the first man using the blood of a defeated god. The Judeo-Christian god preferred to use the dust of the earth. In the Talmudic tradition the dust was kneaded into a shapeless mass (golem) prior to the shaping of the limbs and the infusion of a soul. Prometheus used clay to make the first man and woman, and animated them with fire stolen from heaven.

The Greek god Hephaestus had a mechanical bent. He contrived golden maidservants who looked like real girls, who could speak and walk, and who were filled with intelligence and wisdom (*Iliad*, Book XVIII). Hephaestus also built twenty tripods which 'run by themselves to a meeting of the gods and amaze the company by running home again', and he also constructed the giant Talus out of brass to guard Crete by hugging intruders to death against his heated body. Hence long before the beginning of the Christian epoch, men had speculated on how inanimate substances could be configured to behave with intelligence and purpose.

In more recent times a fictional treatment of artificial intelligence can be found in graphic art, tales, theatre and film. In 1624 Giovanni Battista Bracelli published a remarkable collection of forty-eight pictures of dancers, acrobats and fighters. The drawings were representations of the sorts of images we associate with robots today: the figures appear angular, with flat surfaces, and are evidently constructed from fabricated parts. Fictional tales with a robotic focus were written throughout the nineteenth century until the massive explosion of fantasy and science fiction in the twentieth. For example, *L'Eve Nouvelle* (later known as *L'Eve Future*), written in 1879 by Villiers de l'Isle Adam, depicts a remarkable artificial woman animated by electricity. The author is reported to have said: '. . . my master, Edison, will soon teach you that electricity is as powerful as God'. In another story, *Helen O'Loy*, published by Lester del Ray in 1938, a beautiful android is sent as a housekeeper to two bachelors. The creature falls in love with one of the men and marries him.

One of the most influential fictional treatments of the human automaton theme is Karel Capek's R.U.R. (Rossum's Universal Robots), one of the author's five plays in a utopian vein. R.U.R. was first performed in 1921 in Czechoslovakia, to be published two years later (*robot* derives from the Czech word for worker). The plot focuses on a brilliant scientist called Rossum who creates a family of robots to save man from toil. Eventually, after the robots have been used to kill human beings in war, one of Rossum's colleagues gives the robots emotions – whereupon they rebel at being treated as slaves and soon all human life is destroyed. One critic saw the play as 'the most brilliant satire on our mechanized society'.

However, not all writers wanted to give robots a bad name. One of Isaac Asimov's aims was to show that they need not be the hostile creatures suggested by Capek. Rumour has it that Asimov was so depressed at reading tales of hostile robots that he resolved to portray them as caring creatures with which human beings could become emotionally involved. Thus in *Robbie* (an Asimov short story), young Gloria is distressed that her parents, worried at her growing attachment, have sent her pet robot away. To their comment that 'Robbie was only a machine, just a nasty old machine', Gloria retorts ('fiercely and ungrammatically'): 'He was *not* no machine. He was a *person* just like you and me and he was my *friend.*'

In recent years the theme of artificial intelligence has been explored in many films. One need only think of *Star Wars, Alien, Saturn 3, Forbidden Planet, 2001* and *The Day the Earth Stood Still*. But the modern spate of films with an AI content is only the most recent flowering of a tradition that spans nearly a century. As far back as 1897, Georges Méliès made *Gugusse and the Automaton*, and the first of the many *Frankenstein* films was made in 1910 by J. Searle Dawley. In *Metropolis* (1926), the scientist/magician Rotwang makes a double of Maria, the mediator in the under-

ground city where workers toil in appalling conditions to service
the metropolis above. Rotwang's aim is to counter Maria's efforts
on behalf of the workers. The robot double first resembles a
warrior in gleaming armour; later, when covered in 'flesh', the
device is indistinguishable from Maria. In due course the double is
burnt at the stake. The workers see that it is a robot, and Maria
escapes to carry on the good work. (In the course of the film,
Rotwang declares: 'I have created a machine in the image of man,
that never tires or makes a mistake . . . Now we have no further use
for living workers'.)

Robots in films typically exploit their artificial intelligence to the
detriment of human beings (perhaps this circumstance signals an
underlying pessimism in the culture). Thus various people have a
hard time in *Saturn 3* and *The Black Hole*. In *Westworld* a homici-
dal robot is difficult to stop, and in *Demon Seed* a computer
manages to capture and impregnate a human woman. The celebrated computer Hal in *2001: A Space Odyssey* is ready to override
the wishes of the human crew (Hal: 'I must . . . overrule your
authority, since you are not in any condition to exercise it intelligently'). And in *Dark Star*, a bomb-controlling computer is prepared to engage in philosophic disputation before destroying the
human crew.

The various fictional modes have explored robot and computer
possibilities unhampered by the constraints of the real world. In
imagination, artificial intelligence can accomplish anything, perse-
cute and be subject to persecution. Computers can be friends,
advisors, enemies; sensitive robots can be repressed by humans;
clever machines can take a disturbing interest in our affairs; electronic devices of every sort can manifest wisdom, purpose and
emotion. But in the real world, artificial systems are less competent, constrained by the possibilities of current technology. There
are practical limitations on the scope of intelligent machines. The
limitations are exposed more by the factual history of AI than by
how computers and robots are treated in fiction. When we have
glanced at the extent to which artificial intelligence has been
realised in history, we can understand the essential features of AI:
we can look at a couple of definitions and set these against popular
AI myths.

HISTORY AND AI

Precursors to AI

Just as there are fictional precursors to AI, so there are artefacts in history – elaborate toys, automata, etc – which, while totally unintelligent, convey by metaphor the possibility of intelligent machines. Thus, throughout history mechanical principles have been exploited in devices to create the illusion of animation and intelligence.

In all ages, moving models have been constructed to resemble living creatures. For example, the ancient Greeks, Ethiopians and Chinese built statues and other figures, powered by steam or falling water, to act out sequences of motions. Pindar noted the animated figures which adorned every public street and which seemed 'to breathe in stone, or move their marble feet' (*Olympic Ode*, ca 520 B.C.). Daedalus was said to have devised moving statues worked by quicksilver, which walked in front of the Labyrinth. And according to Vitruvius, Ctesibius discovered a wealth of pneumatic laws in the third century B.C. and 'devised methods of raising water, automatic contrivances and amusing things of many kinds . . . blackbirds singing by means of waterworks and figures that drink and move . . .'. Gullible folk often believed that the devices were truly animate, or even worked by divine agency, but there were also robust sceptics: Celsus, for example, writing in the first century A.D., commented scathingly on magic and animals 'not really living but having the appearance of life'.

The fourth century A.D. saw a golden Buddhist statue, set on a carriage and tended by animated models of Taoist monks. As the carriage moved, the monks circled the Buddha, variously bowing and saluting and throwing incense into a censer. In the seventh century, boats were constructed with animated figures, and eighth-century Chinese records depict the mechanical figure of a monk which reached out, saying 'Alms! Alms!', and conveying coins from its hands into a satchel. In 790 A.D. a wooden otter was devised in China, which was said to be able to catch fish, and in 890 a wooden cat, able to catch rats and dancing tiger-flies, was constructed.

Albertus Magnus (1204-72) is said to have manufactured a life-size animated servant. In one version of the tale, Thomas Aquinas destroyed the automaton when he encountered it in the street, believing it to be the work of the devil. The creature – made of metal, wood, glass, wax and leather – is said to have been able to talk and open the door for visitors. Roger Bacon (1214-94) made a speaking head, to the consternation of the pious; and Leonardo da Vinci (1452-1519) constructed an automatic lion in honour of Louis XII: the lion approached Louis, opened its chest with a claw, and pointed to the fleur-de-lis coat of arms of France. And in the seventeenth century René Descartes built an automaton, 'ma fille Francine', which a sea captain flung from his ship in superstitious dread. The eighteenth century saw animated flute players and talking machines: thus Goethe observed: 'The talking machine of Kempelen is not very loquacious but it pronounces certain childish words very nicely.'

In eighteenth-century Switzerland a number of craftsmen (such as Pierre and Henri-Louis Jaquet-Droz) devised automata that could write, draw pictures and play musical instruments. For instance, the Scribe (1770), an elegantly dressed figure of a child, could write with a quilled pen that it dipped in ink and then moved over the page. This remarkable effect was achieved by an elaborate array of precision cams driven by springs. Similarly, the Draughtsman could produce four drawings, one a portrait of Louis XV. While the activated cams were changing their positions, the automaton used bellows to blow the dust off the drawing paper. The Musician – with moving fingers, heaving breast, glancing eyes, etc – was able to play a miniature organ. The Scribe, Draughtsman and Musician are today held in the Musée d'Art et d'Histoire in Neuchâtel, Switzerland.

The nineteenth century saw a variety of talking machines: for example, Euphonia, a 'bearded Turk' exhibited in the Egyptian Hall in Piccadilly. The device could ask and answer questions, laugh, whisper and sing. The movable mouth carried a flexible tongue and an indiarubber palate. Game-playing automata were also devised in the nineteenth century; and before World War I, the Spanish scientist Leonardo Torres y Quevedo, President of the Academy of Sciences in Madrid, built an electromagnetic automaton which could enable the white king and a rook to mate the black king from any position. This relatively simple end game was seen as a clever accomplishment in classical mechanics. A metal base makes contact with the squares of the board to enable the automaton to be informed, by electric currents, of the king's square. Quevado's son presented the automatic chess player at the 1951 Congress of Cybernetics in Paris. The celebrated cyberneticist Norbert Wiener was defeated by the machine, and it was jokingly remarked that this was the last victory of classical mechanics over modern cybernetics.

Performing robots were built for the London Radio Exhibition of 1932: the automata could speak, smoke cigars and read newspapers. Alpha, a chromium-plated robot made for the Mullard Valve Company, could tell the time and read aloud daily newspapers (prerecorded each day). Eric, inspired by R.U.R., opened the exhibition of the Model Engineer Society (1928). This creature used batteries, two electric motors and a system of belts and pulleys to accomplish a number of limited tasks. He would rise slowly, bow stiffly, and move his head from side to side. A loudspeaker in his throat broadcast words from a wireless. And Elektro, another robot, produced by Westinghouse for the New York World Fair (1939), could achieve twenty-six different movements and respond to spoken commands. The words were converted into electrical impulses used to operate relays governing an array of motors. Activated rubber rollers under each foot enabled Elektro to walk. Sparko, his robot dog, could beg, bark and wag his tail.

The Festival Plaza of Expo '70 in Osaka witnessed a gigantic robot that carried flashing lights and moved its head. The device was contrived as part of an overall cybernetic environment, responding to sound and contributing effects of its own. ONOFF, by contrast, was built from scrap in California to publicise the World Museum at Port Costa. This robot invited people to insert coins whereupon it produced postcards of itself. Afterwards people were conducted into the museum to see the large display of toy robots.

The various mechanical devices – animated statues, robots, toys, etc – were designed to *simulate* living and intelligent systems. In no sense were such artefacts truly intelligent. The development of electronics was to change this situation. For the first time there was the possibility that artificial systems could be configured to embody an intelligent potential. Mechanical, electrical and electromechanical systems were capable of mimicry and nothing more, but the electronics technologies were to allow the fabrication of artefacts able to perform many activities characteristic of intelligent creatures. The history of artificial intelligence is in some sense the history of electronic computers.

History of AI

Artificial intelligence is usually regarded as a subclass of computer science, with the implication that there are also *other* subclasses. One reason for this convention is that we can date the start of the activities which are the focus of current AI work (see below). It has also been found convenient to exclude certain computer activities (eg traditional data processing) from the realm of artificial intelligence. But if an ape or a dolphin were able to compute a complex payroll or actuarial table, we would quickly see such behaviour as evidence for intelligence. In short, our definition of the AI subclass is usually arbitrary. An animal that could do differential equations would be deemed intelligent: a similarly skilled computer would not. And there is also what Hofstadter has called the Tessler Theorem: 'Artificial intelligence is whatever computers can't yet do'. People are reluctant to admit the possibility that artefacts may be intelligent. But perhaps machines are intelligent if, under their own steam, they can simply do sums. In fact they are already accomplishing much more.

The first types of calculating devices were the various forms of the abacus, common in ancient China and Japan. These tools, carrying the familiar rows of beads, were aids for engineers, mathematicians and traders, but in no way could they be considered to be computers: they had no means of storing an internal program of instructions. Such researchers as Pascal (1647) and Samuel Morland (1666) produced effective mechanical calculators (Samuel Pepys commented on the Morland machine: 'Very pretty but not very useful'), and at about the same time Leibniz devised a calculator that could perform multiplication and division.

Charles Babbage, born in 1792, is often represented as the

'father of modern computing'. As such he is also a progenitur of artificial intelligence, though this is rarely said. With Herschel, Babbage created the Royal Astronomical Society in the 1820s, and was obliged to compile reference tables (Babbage: 'I wish to God these calculations had been executed by steam'). He contrived two of the most ambitious calculating machines, celebrating the project in 1822 with a paper to the Society ('Observations on the Application of Machinery to the Computation of Mathematical Tables'). At this time he also wrote to Sir Humphrey Davy, president of the Royal Society, proposing that a machine could be developed to replace 'one of the lowest occupations of the human intellect'.

In due course, Babbage developed with mixed success two machines: the *Difference Engine* and the more ambitious *Analytical Engine*. A young Italian military engineer, L. F. Menabrea, described the latter machine in 1842 (in a paper written in French). Ada Lovelace, Babbage's co-worker for many years, translated the paper and added her own detailed additions. These included programs which she had originated. The original paper was greatly expanded and the power of the Analytical Engine was evident. Its central importance for the future of electronic computing was that it demonstrated, albeit in mechanical terms, the components that were essential in any general-purpose computer system: *input* (allowing numbers to be fed into the machine), *store* (to hold numbers and program instructions), *arithmetic unit* (to perform the calculations), *control unit* (to control task performance under the direction of the stored program), and *output* (to make the results of the processing available to the users).

The tabulator designed by Dr. Herman Hollerith, as an effective device for analysing the 1890 American census, was the first computing machine to use non-mechanical processing means. This approach, allowing an electric current to advance a counter by one, was exploited by International Business Machines (IBM) in its early days. In 1892, William Burroughs introduced the first commercially available adding machine, but it was not until the early-1940s that it proved possible, following the work of Vannevar Bush with thermionic valves, to use electronic components as elements in digital computing circuits. The scene was set for the rapid development of the modern electronic digital computer.

Binary operations were introduced by Konrad Zuse in 1935 into the Z1 computer, an entirely mechanical device. The Z2 used electromechanical relays instead of mechanical switches and employed punched paper tape as input. The IBM Mark 1 (1943) was also based on electromagnetic relays, and in the same year Colossus 1 began use in Britain to decipher the messages generated by Enigma, the German code system. Some of the brilliant young men (eg Turing and Michie) involved in code breaking were to become immensely influential in the development of artificial intelligence.

The 1940s also witnessed the emergence of the Electronic Numerical Integrator and Calculator (ENIAC), designed with 18,000 thermionic valves to compute ballistics tables for guns and missiles. ENIAC weighed 30 tons and needed to be housed in a room 60ft by 25ft. The computer was less powerful than any modest micro of the 1980s. In 1945, John von Neumann began the design of the Electronic Discrete Variable Automatic Computer (EDVAC), and for the first time the notion of stored-program control was incorporated into the design of an electronic digital computer. Von Neumann was to stimulate one intriguing thread in the AI debate by positing the concept of *self-replicating* computer systems. In the same spirit, in 1948, Norbert Wiener advanced the highly influential doctrine that a new science, *cybernetics,* was equally relevant to self-governing biological and artificial systems. The ground was being prepared for the analysis of certain types of computer systems in terms of animal psychology and behaviour.

Second-generation computers, based on the transistor rather than the glass valve, were developed in the 1950s. For example, the Ferranti Mark 1, the Lyons Electronic Office (LEO) and the Ferranti Mercury all became active at this time, and this type of computer technology continued to be commercially dominant throughout the 1960s. By the early-1970s it was clear, with the capacity to build thousands of effective transistors onto a miniscule silicon chip, that computers would become smaller and more powerful. Such third-generation technology began to give way to fourth-generation designs in the 1980s, as circuit integration became denser and new programming languages were developed. The early-1980s also saw the framing of plans for an ambitious fifth generation of computers (see Simons, 1983) in which many aspects of artificial intelligence were intended to play a central part.

One of the most significant threads in the emergence of AI is associated with the name of Alan Turing. In 1937 he published a seminal paper on 'computable numbers', in which the concept of the 'universal Turing machine' was launched. Here it was proposed that a machine could carry out any mathematical procedure, providing the machine was supplied with an adequate instruction table (the equivalent of the modern computer program). The model that Turing had so skilfully presented was so general that it served to describe all the computers that were to emerge in the decades ahead. The 'computable numbers' paper is now recognised as one of the most important milestones in the history of computer science. But more was to come.

After working at Bletchley Park on code breaking during the war, Turing went to the National Physical Laboratory, Teddington, to help to design the Automatic Computing Engine (ACE). But administrative problems led to delays, and Turing went back to Cambridge in 1947 for a sabbatical. Here he developed his ideas that an ACE system would be able to model the actions carried out by the human brain, and produced a startlingly prophetic paper on artificial intelligence. In this paper, 'Computing Machinery and Intelligence', Turing directly addresses the question of whether machines could think, and he observes:

'. . . I believe that at the end of the century the use of words and general educated opinion will have altered so much that one will be able to speak of machines thinking without expecting to be contradicted.'

He begins the paper with what he calls the 'imitation game', a ploy that is today known as the *Turing test*. Here an interrogator is separated from a person (or a machine) under interrogation, and communication is only possible using a teletype. The idea is that if the human cannot tell, through the interrogation, whether the communication is with another person or a machine, then the machine – if indeed it *is* a machine giving the answers – may be regarded as intelligent. Turing was well aware that many people would find absurd the notion that a machine could be intelligent. So he anticipated some of the objections and answered them (see Objections and Myths, below). Turing, with David Champernowne (who later worked on how computers might compose music), also wrote the first chess-playing program, 'Turochamp'.

The administrative difficulties that beset Alan Turing were also to afflict Donald Michie in Edinburgh and other AI researchers. In 1973 the report by Sir James Lighthill in the UK declared AI work unfruitful and undeserving of government funds. Work in Great Britain on artificial intelligence received a colossal blow from which it has not yet recovered. A belated attempt to remedy the situation has been made with the distribution of funds under the 1983/4 Alvey initiative. But, with regard to the potential of AI, a number of countries – notably the United States and Japan – showed more prescience through the 1970s.

We have seen that the history of artificial intelligence is in some sense the history of computer science. At the same time it is useful to chart the origins of AI as a subclass discipline. The term 'artificial intelligence' is usually regarded as having been invented by John McCarthy in 1956, then assistant professor of mathematics at Dartmouth College in Hanover, N.H. At that time he convened a conference which is seen as the beginning of AI as a separate branch of computer science. The aim was to bring together serious researchers in the field and to establish effective communication between them. A number of those who attended – Allen Newell, Herbert Simon, Marvin Minsky and John McCarthy himself – are now universally recognised as leading AI pioneers.

Newell and Simon reported work that they had carried out at the Carnegie Institute of Technology in Pittsburgh (now Carnegie-Mellon University). They had developed the (now celebrated) theorem-proving Logic Theorist, the first computer program to process symbols rather than numerical quantities. This became recognised as the first effective AI program. Working with J. C. Shaw of the Rand Corporation, Newell and Simon had developed the Information Processing Language (IPL), the first language which enabled computers to process concepts. The use of IPL to build the Logic Theorist was a major step towards the automation of cognitive thought.

Marvin Minsky, who had worked with Claude Shannon at Bell Laboratories, was to stimulate AI development under Project MAC at the Massachusetts Institute of Technology. He is a co-founder of the MIT AI Group which later became the MIT AI

Laboratory. John McCarthy, another co-founder of the AI Group and now at Stanford University, is the inventor of the Lisp (list processing) language, one of the most favoured AI programming languages.

During the 1970s Edward Feigenbaum, also at Stanford, developed the first expert system, Dendral, used to analyse mass spectrography data (see Chapter 8). And another Stanford professor, Terry Winograd, produced a program (called SHRDLU) which was able to manipulate simulated objects shaped like wooden blocks. This program, much cited in the AI literature, could be told about the simulated blocks and asked to rearrange them. Dendral and SHRDLU were early examples of programs designed to behave intelligently in particular worlds. Such programs aim to focus on a particular task and they do not exhibit the generality of response thought by some observers to characterise the truly intelligent system.

It now seems clear that early AI research concentrated unduly on general problem-solving. The early efforts were largely unsuccessful because of the combinatorial explosion, the fact that exhaustive searches of a problem domain were soon lost in possible paths whose number grew exponentially. People do not attempt to solve problems in this way. Instead they rely upon knowledge that is relevant to the problem in question. It was soon realised that perhaps computers could be programmed to solve well-defined problems in a similar fashion. This led to a new emphasis on studying how knowledge could be represented in computer systems and inferences drawn from it. Through the 1970s a main AI theme was the study of *knowledge-based systems* (see Chapter 5), often referred to as 'expert systems'. Other AI interest focused on such things as language translation, game playing and robot behaviour.

In August 1981, Minsky, McCarthy, Newell and others from the Dartmouth conference held a meeting to celebrate the twenty-fifth anniversary of the pioneering encounter. The meeting was held at the University of British Columbia, Vancouver, during the seventh International Joint Conference on Artificial Intelligence (IJCAI). More than twenty nations were represented at the international conference, including the USA, USSR, East and West Germany,

Sweden, Israel and India. Over a five-day period, more than 200 papers and panel discussions were presented, and the topics included: expert systems, knowledge representation, inference, search methods, learning, natural language, medical applications and artificial vision. We may take it as highly significant that many of the papers had a clear psychological or biological relevance.

Today many large companies – IBM, Hewlett-Packard, Digital Equipment Corporation, Tektronix, Fujitsu, Hitachi, etc – have set up AI research laboratories; and important research is being conducted at many institutes and universities (for example, at Stanford, MIT and Carnegie-Mellon in the US, and at Edinburgh and Sussex in the UK). The Japanese plans for fifth-generation computers require massive funding in AI research and development (see Simons, 1983), and increasing commercial emphasis is being given to the development of particular expert systems for specific purposes (medical diagnosis, crop disease diagnosis, geological prospecting, electronic circuit analysis, chemical synthesis, etc). Inevitably, military organisations are keen to fund research and development work that will lead to artificially-intelligent weaponry.

Computer systems based on AI techniques are now available as aids for a wide range of professional workers: mathematicians, engineers, doctors, teachers, chemists, geologists, biologists, lawyers, office and factory managers, etc. There is a growing recognition that AI facilities will become essential to commercial success. It is important in this context that such facilities need not be expensive. In fact, expert-systems software is now available for microcomputers.

WHAT IS AI?

It is useful, partly by way of summary, to indicate what is meant by artificial intelligence. We have seen (Chapter 1) that *intelligence* itself is a difficult enough concept. The word 'intelligence' derives from the Latin *legere*, meaning to gather, to collect, to assemble. *Intellegere* is generally taken to mean to choose among, hence to understand, perceive and know. Feigenbaum and McCorduck (1983) comment: 'If we can imagine an artifact that can collect, assemble, choose among, understand, perceive, and know, then we have an artificial intelligence.'

The definition of AI that is favoured depends upon the person's interest. Thus Margaret Boden (1977) declares: 'One thing, however, is certain: artificial intelligence is not the study of computers. Computers are metallic machines of intrinsic interest to electronic engineers but not, as such, to many others. So if you are not enamored of tin cans, you need not fear to meet any in this book'. By *artificial intelligence*, Boden means 'the use of computer programs and programming techniques to cast light on the principles of intelligence in general and human thought in particular'. The idea is that the expression can be used 'as a generic term to cover all machine research that is somehow relevant to human knowledge and psychology . . .'. With this approach the emphasis is on software: it even seems to be imagined that when one has written a suitable coded sequence of instructions one has created a certain type of AI 'machine'. But not all AI researchers regard computers as relatively unimportant: the tin-can image of hardware is not universal. A program can, for example, *simulate* the behaviour of a robot, but the program is of no practical value if there is no suitable physical system on which it can be run. Marvin Minsky, in a much-quoted definition, has suggested the practical character of AI:

'Artificial intelligence is the science of making machines do things that would require intelligence if done by men.'

But this definition says nothing about the nature of intelligence. As we have seen, the human ability to perform complex calculations would normally be regarded as requiring intelligence, but AI researchers would rarely include computation of this sort as falling within the province of artificial intelligence.

We have already indicated something of the character of AI by listing some typical activities which interest researchers in the field, ie such activities as problem solving, perception and game-playing. Another approach is to list the aims of artificial intelligence in more general terms. In this way an effective definition of AI can be given. Aaron Sloman (1978), for example, sees three main aims of artificial intelligence:

— theoretical analysis of possible effective explanations of intelligent behaviour;

— explaining human abilities;

— construction of intelligent artefacts.

These broad aims invite many further questions. Sloman himself suggests various considerations in the twelve succinct paragraphs that follow. It is recognised that intelligent behaviour is concerned with the ability 'to build, describe, interpret, compare, modify and use complex structures, including symbolic structures like sentences, pictures, maps and plans for action'. Moreover, AI research that is domain-specific is bound to overlap with research in other disciplines, most of which have a human reference (eg psychology, education, anthropology and physiology). It is impossible, for example, to make a computer understand natural language (say, English or Japanese) without studying syntax and semantics (ie without exploring linguistics).

The difficulty in defining artificial intelligence derives from two main factors. The first is that *intelligence* itself is ill-defined and little understood; and the second is that many human beings have a deep-seated reluctance to admit that artefacts may develop 'mental' attributes. This second reason inevitably confuses the definition game: whatever computers accomplish, sceptics are constantly looking towards the unfulfilled achievements that constitute *real* intelligence. However, it is clear that the more computer abilities approach those of human beings the harder it will be to argue that computers do not behave in a truly intelligent fashion.

WHAT COMPUTERS CAN DO

Many of the early claims of the AI enthusiasts are still unrealised. For example, there is still no universal language translator, and the world chess champion is still a human being. At the same time, important AI advances have been made in a number of different fields, including:

— automatic language translation;

— game-playing (in chess, backgammon, bridge, poker, etc);

— theorem-proving (in symbolic logic and elementary geometry);

— reading handwritten or printed characters;

— recognition of items in a photograph or sketch;

— recognition of human faces (even when assuming different expressions);

— recognition of spoken words and continuous speech;

— understanding natural languages (answering questions and producing summaries of pieces of text);

— writing poetry (eg haiku) and short stories;

— composing musical melodies and harmonisations;

— analogical thinking (eg using geometrical shapes);

— diagnosis of diseases and electrical-circuit faults.

In one profile of computer competence (Winston, 1979) it is pointed out that computers can variously:

— perform geometric intelligence tests;

— learn in mathematical, geometric and other fields;

— understand simple drawings;

— understand simple English;

— solve problems in mathematical, chemical, medical and other fields;

— understand electronic circuits;

— do useful industrial work;

— model human psychological processes.

In summary, Winston, writing several years ago, comments that computers can already do many things that require intelligence: 'They can solve many problems like experts, reason geometrically, solve problems in mathematics, learn simple concepts, understand simple drawings, engage in simple dialogue, and do useful work'. Today, with the growing interest in expert systems and the momentum of the Japanese fifth-generation programme there is an increasing recognition of the scope of intelligent artefacts.

OBJECTIONS AND MYTHS

There are various objections to the idea of machine intelligence. Some are nothing more than emotional spasms, others purport to be cogently argued. But since most of the objections are based on myths, they say more about human vanity under threat than about the potential of intelligent artefacts.

Alan Turing, one of the first to espouse the AI cause, was quick to recognise possible objections. In his famous 1950 paper he cites nine objections to the idea that machines could think, and presents counter-comments in each case:

— *the theological objection* suggests that no animal or machine can think because God has only given souls to men and women (Turing: 'I am unable to accept any part of this . . . I am not very impressed with theological arguments whatever they may be used to support');

— *the "heads in the sand" objection* suggests that the consequences of machines thinking would be too dreadful ('I do not think that this argument is sufficiently substantial to require refutation');

— *the mathematical objection* cites Gödel's theorem to show that there are necessary limitations to the power of artificial systems (' . . . it has only been stated, without any sort of proof, that no such limitations apply to the human intellect');

— *the argument from consciousness* as represented, for example, in Professor Jefferson's Lister Oration (1949): 'Not until a machine can write a sonnet or compose a concerto because of thoughts and emotions felt . . . could we agree that machine equals brain . . . No mechanism could feel . . . pleasure at its successes, grief when its valves fuse, be warmed by flattery, be made miserable by its mistakes, be charmed by sex, be angry or depressed when it cannot get what it wants'. Turing comments that this argument relies upon a solipsist posture (' . . . the only way to know that a *man* thinks is to be that particular man'), and he concludes: 'I think that most of those who support the argument from consciousness could be persuaded to abandon it rather than be forced into the solipsist position';

— *arguments from various disabilities* suggest that however competent machines become they will always be unable to do particular things, like 'be kind, resourceful, beautiful, friendly . . . have initiative, have a sense of humour, tell right from wrong, make mistakes . . . fall in love, enjoy strawberries and cream . . . make someone fall in love . . . learn from experience . . . use words properly, be the subject of its own thought . . . have as much diversity of behaviour as a man, do something really new . . . '. Turing observes caustically that no support is usually offered for these statements and that they mostly boil down to forms of the argument from consciousness;

— *Lady Lovelace's objection* ('The Analytical Engine has no pretensions to *orginate* anything. It can do *whatever we know how to order it* to perform') implies that machines are mindless slaves, incapable of any degree of intelligence. After a slight detour, Turing arrives back at the argument from consciousness ('It is a line of argument that we must consider closed'). Today we are sufficiently aware of computers accomplishing new things not to attach much weight to this objection;

— *the argument from continuity in the nervous system* suggests that, since a small error in the information about the size of a nervous impulse impinging on a neuron may significantly affect the size of the outgoing impulse, it is impossible to mimic the behaviour of the nervous system with a discrete state machine (Turing: ' . . . if we adhere to the conditions of the imitation game, the interrogater will not be able to take any advantage of this difference');

— *the argument from informality of behaviour* suggests that it is impossible to provide a set of rules to indicate what a person should do in every conceivable set of circumstances, and so people are not machines. Here Turing emphasises that we will only find such rules through scientific observation, and we know of no circumstances where we may claim to have searched enough. Moreover would anyone expect to be able to understand totally a computer program by examining a limited number of computer responses. Talking of computer output, Turing comments: 'I would defy anyone to learn from these replies sufficient about the program to be able to predict any replies to untried values';

— *the argument from sensory perception* suggests that human beings have powers not available to machines. Perhaps surprisingly, Turing finds this argument 'quite a strong one' ('If telepathy is admitted it will be necessary to tighten our test'). Later AI workers (eg Hofstadter, 1979 – 'My own point of view . . . is that ESP does not exist') have been less impressed than Turing by this sort of argument.

Many of the objections to AI expressed more recently are either restatements of, or versions of, the objections discussed by Turing in 1950. For example, objections cited in *The Robots are Coming* (NCC Publications, 1974) can be related directly to the Turing objections:

— thinking is by definition something done by man only (compare with *the theological objection*);

— it would be most unfortunate if machines could think (*the 'head in the sands' objection*);

— a computer can do no more than its programmer makes it do (*Lady Lovelace's objection*).

In response to such objections it can be further remarked that the question of whether computers can think is partly a semantic matter: define 'thinking' one way and computers can do it, define it another way and thinking is beyond their competence. It can also be pointed out that the Lady Lovelace objection fails to take into account that human beings themselves are programmed – by a complex of genetic endowment, early upbringing, education, etc. The deterministic constraints on computer behaviour can be found *mutatis mutandis* on human behaviour also.

The objections to AI are sometimes criticised as involving mistaken ideas about computers. Thus Raphael (1976) highlights two 'misleading myths' of this sort. Firstly there is the idea that *a computer is nothing but a big fast arithmetic machine*. Here it is pointed out that though computers can of course do arithmetic they can also perform many other types of operations. The instruction set of a typical computer includes such operations as LOAD, TEST, SHIFT, READ, SKIP, MATCH, MASK, TRANSFER, etc. Today there is considerable emphasis on computers being symbol-manipulating machines, an approach which does not limit their vast computational competence but which also allows them to form concepts, to take decisions, to solve problems and to interpret perceptual data from the outside world.

The second myth, an obvious variant on the Lady Lovelace objection, is that computers are nothing more than obedient slaves, equipped only to do what they are told. Again there is a trivial sense in which this is true. No machine (or animal) can act beyond or outside its programming, but the question as to whether a computer can be *original*, ie achieve *new* things, is open to empirical investigation. In fact there are many instances where computers have achieved new knowledge and new insights. One need only think of the Samuel draughts program (which exhibited a learning capacity), the Lenat mathematical program (which came across maximally divisible numbers not formerly considered by Lenat and most other mathematicians), the Prospector expert system (which, in conflict with human experts, was eventually proved right), and chess programs (such as the Chess Champion Mark V) which have found chess solutions unknown to any human being.

Winston (1979) lists various 'myths about thinking' that by now will be familiar. He identifies these as:

— *Computers can never* ... (' ... the standard proof is as weak as it is inevitable'). Merely because computers have so far not achieved particular things, it does not mean that they will not do so in the future (' ... someday computers may laugh at us and wonder if biological information processors could be really smart');

— *Computers are not intelligent because they do not write like Shakespeare, compose like Beethoven, do science like Newton*. This is clearly a variant on the 'computers can never ... ' argument;

— *Computers can only do what they are programmed to do* (Lady Lovelace again);

— *Software can never equal brainware because transistors are different from neurons*. This again is amenable to empirical testing. What in reality are the actual accomplishments of computer systems? And what are the trends?;

— *Probabilistic machinery causes inspiration and explains free will.* The idea is that random neural behaviour allows important human creative activity (Winston: 'It is more likely that increased randomness of neural behaviour is the problem of the epileptic and the drunk, not the advantage of the brilliant');

— *Computers can never appreciate aesthetics.* A variant on the 'computers can never . . .' argument;

— *Intelligence can never be understood.* We have already considered the problems of defining intelligence, but this argument is a cop-out. Its advocates would still be willing to declare this or that individual 'intelligent' – or, if they baulked at that word, to call someone 'competent', 'skilful', 'perceptive', 'sharp', 'expert', etc.

In many other works (eg Feigenbaum and McCorduck, 1983) the objections and myths, and their variants, are rehearsed – usually so that they can be exposed as fallacious. The situation seems to boil down to two basic considerations. Firstly, human vanity is threatened by the prospect of intelligent machines. This stimulates efforts to find reasons why computers will always be intellectually inferior to human beings. Secondly, current limitations on computer performance tell us nothing about the constraints on computer behaviour tomorrow. Already there have been staggering computer developments in only forty years. Where will computers get to in four hundred years? In four thousand?

SUMMARY

This chapter has indicated some of the fictional and factual precursors to artificial intelligence. We see that the notion of AI runs back thousands of years in human history but that only in the modern age was it possible to devise artefacts, typically relying upon electronic circuits, that could realistically be regarded as intelligent.

Some indication has been given of the areas of AI interest, the types of activities on which artificially-intelligent systems are currently engaged. It is recognised that there is hostility to the idea of intelligent machines and some of the reasons for this are given. Typical objections ('misleading myths', 'myths of the mind') are indicated, and some fallacies and confusions in these objections are given. People are naturally disturbed by the accelerating pace of technological innovation, particularly where new artefacts appear as an intellectual threat to human self-image. But it seems clear that intelligent machines, designed and built by human beings, are already working among us; and that their competence will develop rapidly in the years ahead.

Part 2

OBJECTIVES AND METHODS

3 Psychology and Cognition

INTRODUCTION

There is a reciprocal influence between modern psychology research and work in artificial intelligence. A central aim of AI is to model, simulate, mimic or duplicate psychological phenomena; and research in psychology aims to develop models and techniques that deepen our understanding of mental processes in human beings and other animals. Zenon Pylyshyn (1981), a celebrated AI worker, has pointed out that 'the field of AI is coextensive with that of cognitive psychology . . . as intellectual disciplines (not applied technologies), both fields are concerned with the same problems and thus must ultimately be judged by the same criteria of success'. It is emphasised that the ultimate goal, in each case, is 'a better understanding of intelligence'.

Cognitive psychology has developed in recent years largely because computer science has encouraged researchers to view the physiological brain as an information-processing mechanism (Pylyshyn: 'I believe that AI is just the medicine that cognitive psychology needs at this stage in its development'). Artificial intelligence, as a subclass of computer science, has reinforced an information-processing model of the human mind, so opening new avenues of enquiry in psychology and related disciplines. Allport (1980) has even gone so far as to claim 'the advent of Artificial Intelligence is the single most important development in the history of psychology . . . it seems to me not unreasonable to expect that Artificial Intelligence will ultimately come to play the role vis à vis the psychological and social sciences that mathematics, from the seventeenth century on, has done for the physical sciences'.

This chapter assumes that artificial intelligence research is concerned with building systems that are capable of psychological
behaviour. This approach should not be seen as limited in principle
to any particular mental phenomenon, ie AI can be regarded as
embracing emotion, humour and self-knowledge, as well as the
more obvious AI concerns (such as problem-solving and
decision-making). It is possible, for example, to develop an
information-processing theory of emotion (see Other Mental
Attributes, below) just as it is possible to develop a computational
theory of perception. A study of cognitive psychology, in its various aspects, helps to reveal the potential for intelligent machines.

THE EMERGENCE OF COGNITIVE PSYCHOLOGY

The origins of scientific psychology are usually traced to Wilhelm
Wundt. He created a psychology laboratory in 1879 at the University of Leipzig, and his methods were influential for several
decades. In particular, he argued that psychology research should
employ the techniques of science, though later researchers were to
point out that he betrayed this edict by relying excessively on
introspective methods. Wundt would ask people to describe their
thoughts as they performed specific tasks, and the information
obtained in this way would be used in the analysis of consciousness.

The reaction against Wundt's introspective psychology (an early
form of structuralism) led to *behaviourism*, represented histori-
cally by Pavlov in Russia and John Watson in America. Behaviourism, well established by 1920, largely ignored introspective tes-
timony, concentrating instead on the close observation of
behaviour in laboratory conditions. Since only behaviour could be
directly observed it was regarded as the only legitimate concern of
psychology researchers.

By contrast, *gestalt psychology*, another reaction to Wundt's
structuralism, aimed to preserve the interest in internal mental
processes and structures but with a more rigorous scientific control. However, this line of enquiry foundered, mainly because the
required scientific tools were not available. It has been pointed out
(eg by Mayer, 1981) that the gestalt psychologists asked many of
the same questions that cognitive psychologists ask today, but now
there are the tools 'to answer at least some of them successfully'.

(The development of *psychoanalytic theory*, under the influence of Sigmund Freud, was largely a therapeutic endeavour, a part of medical science. It has done little to explain human feelings and emotions, its main concern.)

By the late-1940s it was increasingly recognised that behaviourism was unduly restrictive. It did not permit any speculation about what might be called the 'architecture of cognition'. The human mind was a 'black box', able to accept inputs ('stimuli') and to emit outputs ('responses'), but within which nothing could be scientifically deemed to occur. But there was a growing feeling among researchers that it would be useful to speculate about the internal processes and structures of the human mind. Gestalt psychology and psychoanalytic theory, in Europe torn apart by the war years, were not generally regarded as helpful. The time was ripe for a fresh initiative in psychology theory and research, but a new route had to be found.

A number of important developments in the 1940s and 1950s were to stimulate the emergence of a modern cognitive psychology. These influences suggested an approach to psychological research that would at once have the necessary scientific rigour and also be sufficiently fertile in stimulating new theoretical structures and experimental programmes. Four main influences, originating during this period but having lasting significance, can be identified:

— the *electronic digital computer* emerged in the 1940s and began a period of rapid evolution. It was obvious that the computer could do many of the things that were characteristic of the human mind, such as collect, store and manipulate information, as well as learn, use language, reason, take decisions and solve problems. An effort was made to reinterpret old psychological problems in terms of new computer analogies. And again it became legitimate to explore internal mental processes and structures: they could now be specified in terms of computer programs;

— the *mathematical theory of communication* appeared to offer a content-independent measure of psychological capacity and mental activity. Using units such as bits-per-second there were many early attempts (eg Quastler, 1956) to determine the maximum information-transmission capability of the human being;

— new work in *linguistics* encouraged the shift away from behaviourist theories of language and towards analysis in terms of underlying cognitive structures. Chomsky (1957) offered a cognitive analysis of various aspects of language behaviour. This approach was to influence efforts to give machines a comprehension of languages;

— the *biological approach* of Piaget (1954) encouraged attention to the internal processes and structures that underlie developmental changes in human behaviour. The Piaget approach derived support from parallel developments in such sciences as neurophysiology and biochemistry: consider, for example, the new significance of information transmission in genetic theory.

Of these various influences, the computer impact was dominant. The idea of 'mental computation' suggested a framework within which explanations of all types of mental processes could be usefully sought. Many of the new computer concepts became standard ideas in cognitive (ie information-processing) psychology. Thus the models of human information processing of the 1950s and 1960s included such ideas as the separation of active processor and passive storage, the use of a fixed-capacity central processor for all mental operations, and the storage of both data and program routines in a memory. Where, subsequently, researchers felt compelled to move away from some of these early concepts, they developed further metaphors from new aspects of computer science. One example of this is where increased attention was given to 'distributed processing' mechanisms: there was a convenient correlation between the localisation of functions revealed by neurophysiology and the emerging computer pattern of distributed intelligence in a factory or office complex. Cognitive psychology was able to evolve without straying from the computer-type metaphors that had helped to bring about its birth.

The 1950s and 1960s saw a number of landmark papers that extended the framework of cognitive psychology. In 1956, Miller produced a landmark paper that supported the concept of an information-processing model of the human mind. This paper, drawing on both computer science and information theory, proposed constraints on human processing capability (' . . . the span of absolute judgement and the span of immediate memory impose severe limitations on the amount of information that we are able to receive, process and remember'). In the same spirit, Newell, Shaw and Simon (1958) helped to characterise traditional psychological questions in terms of analogies drawn from modern computing. And in 1960 Miller and co-workers proposed a cognitive approach based on the idea that the unit of behaviour is a *plan*, involving feedback loops similar to those used in computers. In this model, man becomes an active processor of information. Neisser (1967) produced a successful textbook on cognitive psychology, using the (by then) familiar notion of distinct memory stores and processes, and focusing on the question of perception.

The new ideas were sufficiently compelling to encourage researchers to view human mental activity as directly analogous to what went on in a computer. One writer (Hunt, 1971) was able to ask 'What kind of a computer is man?' and to begin the task of describing a computing system that 'thinks like a man'. The rapid development of cognitive psychology had encouraged the view that even human thought could be adequately described in terms of information processing. It became increasingly plausible to view the human mind as an automaton.

THE MIND AS AUTOMATON

Information and Cybernetics

In 1972 the psychologist George Miller pointed out that "Many psychologists have come to take for granted in recent years . . . that men and computers are merely two different species of a more abstract genus called 'information processing systems'." The implication was that 'The concepts that describe abstract information processing systems must, perforce, describe any particular examples of such systems'. It seemed increasingly clear that if man as a species was mainly interested in the processing of information then any machine that could be induced to process information in appropriate ways would acquire mental properties. Such a machine was the digital computer.

Another parallel theme was concerned with developing the idea that man was an *automaton*. In one view (eg Sampson, 1975), automata theory is concerned with the relations between computers and their languages. Here a computer is seen as a physical realisation of an abstract entity, the mathematical system called an 'automaton'. (This clearly conflicts with common usage where *automata* are akin to robots, physical systems behaving in preprogrammed paths.)

The automaton may be regarded as a device 'defined by input rules which specify how an input sentence moves it from one state to another, computing rules which specify how it passes through different states spontaneously . . . and output rules which specify that entry to certain states causes it to produce output'. The human mind may be depicted as an automaton with its various states corresponding to the various structures of knowledge and belief. The input rules define the effect of what one hears on one's beliefs, and the computing rules define what we generally understand as *thinking* in its various forms and manifestations.

Sampson (1975) takes care to point out that the human automaton only deals with 'those small subparts of people's minds' that are concerned with explicit propositional knowledge or belief. This implies that such mental aspects as emotion or attentiveness are outside the province of automata theory, but there is no obvious reason why this should be so. If an area of mental activity can be described in information-processing (ie cognitive) terms then it is amenable to being analysed as characteristic of an automaton. And there are plenty of cognitive theories of emotion that could be exploited for this purpose (see Strongman, 1978).

The information-processing and automaton views of the human mind gain indirect support from research in cybernetics, the study of control and communications mechanisms in artificial and biological systems. Cybernetic systems are regarded as self-regulating systems that operate using feedback controls. Artificial cybernetic systems include servomechanisms which comprise receptors (to accept feedback information) and comparators (which measure the difference between the information received and a predetermined value that helps to define a course of action). The system then makes compensatory changes to remove any detected difference, so steering the machine behaviour on the required course.

The higher animals have many functional servomechanisms, most of which involve the brain and other components of the central nervous system. For example, in mammals the cerebellum is an effective servomechanism that allows an animal to maintain a smooth course of muscular activity. Other animal servomechanisms may use the medulla and other brain areas, with feedback information provided via the senses, skin conductivity, the blood stream, etc.

The development of cybernetics as a discipline that can equally describe the behaviour of the central nervous system and computer operations reinforces the idea that mental activity is within the scope of artificial systems. Norbert Wiener and other researchers in the 1940s and 1950s saw that certain biological and machine processes could be described in the same terms. Today workers in artificial intelligence are extending this basic concept in connection with cognitive operations.

Components for Thought

From a cybernetic point of view – and from the point of view also of artificial intelligence – the active components for thought can be any physical array capable of sustaining the necessary processes. Information can be handled by silicon circuits or by neuron networks, but perhaps in vastly dissimilar ways. It is sometimes pointed out that the thousands of millions of neurons in the human brain can result in possibly one quadrillion connections: moreover the average neuron, according to Dr. William Shoemaker of the Salk Institute, is as complex as an entire minicomputer. This may be misleading – a single neuron can be effectively modelled by a relatively small number of electronic components – but it does make us careful to avoid facile comparisons with computer circuits and brain 'wiring'.

We do not need to pursue the ways in which neurons process information (see, for example, Lindsay and Norman, 1977, Chapter 6). It is enough that neuron function is today approached almost exclusively in terms of control and communication theory (ie in terms of cybernetics). Neurons, unlike silicon circuits, depend for their effectiveness upon both electrical activity (eg the transfer of ions across a membrane) and chemical response. But the overall scheme is the same for both artificial and biological systems: information, coded and shaped in particular ways, is transmitted and stored in a manner appropriate to the system. The various electrical, electronic and chemical activities are all means to the same end – the controlled manipulation of information.

That the brain (or the mind) is an information-processing automaton, akin to the theoretical and physical automata that engage the interest of AI researchers, says nothing about the character of the information-processing activity. The 'thought' of which the system is capable needs to be studied for its nature to be understood. For example, a system may think but not be conscious: Allport (1980) has given an engaging account of 'unconscious' information-processing in human beings; and information-processing artefacts may or may not be conscious, according to how we choose to recognise such a condition.

Thinking can be achieved, in principle, by any configuration of physical components that is capable of processing information in appropriate ways. It still remains to examine the configuration to ascertain how it accomplishes the various cognitive tasks (eg perception, storing, learning, problem solving, decision-making, etc). Studies of the biological brain and possible computer designs can be mutually helpful, but findings and metaphors from one type of system should not be glibly imposed on another.

MODES OF PERCEPTION

General

Perceptual ability, common in animals and many other life-forms, is now evolving in various ways for computer-based systems. There are, for example, many advantages in providing computer-controlled robots with visual and tactile abilities: in this way robot versatility can be enhanced and automated facilities rendered more adaptable in a changing environment.

The five human senses allow information about the world to be fed to the brain. The incoming information is then evaluated (eg compared with existing stored knowledge) to allow perception to occur. Hence it is the brain that perceives, not the senses. *How* the brain interprets the incoming information is obviously central to the human being's efficiency in functioning in the world. And any insight into human perception is obviously relevant to the possibility of building a perceptual ability into artificial systems.

In machines, perception is often called *pattern recognition*, a phrase that immediately suggests the comparison of incoming information with stored knowledge ('recognition' implies prior experience). Various techniques can be used in animals and machines to facilitate the recognition task. For example, *template matching* is one of the simplest schemes for classifying and recognising patterns. Here there must be a template, appropriate to the particular mode of perception, for each of the patterns to be recognised. As a simple example for visual perception an individual letter (say, A) might excite a particular pattern of receptors on the retina. If these specific receptors were connected to a single detector cell, this configuration (receptors plus detector) would represent a template able to detect the letter A. Other configurations would be concerned with detecting other letters.

However, the template model of human perception is usually dismissed as inadequate. With this approach there would be problems, for instance, if the letter were printed too big, too small, crooked or in 'fuzzy' type. More templates could be added to the configuration to cope with these difficulties but this may lead to endless complications. In fact many computer systems use a template method for pattern recognition, relying on *preprocessing* before trying to match the pattern of incoming signals. Here a letter may be first rotated so that its long axis is vertically oriented, then scaled in size before matching with a set of stored templates. Perhaps the best known use of automatic pattern recognition is where characters on bank cheques are scanned by computer-based equipment.

The template system is *data-driven*: nothing happens until the data is supplied, whereupon it is processed to yield an answer. Another approach is for the system (animal or machine) to conceive what the incoming information might represent, in order to aid the subsequent recognition process. In this case the processing is termed *concept-driven*: a conceptualisation occurs, after which the system looks for evidence to confirm the expectation. Data-driven and concept-driven techniques often work together.

It is not difficult to see the problems that afflict the perceptual process. Incoming information may be partial, intermittent or a confusing mixture of relevant and irrelevant signals. Information stored for reference purposes may similarly be incomplete or mixed with other data, making it difficult to achieve a clear matching result. And what is true of visual perception is true also, *mutatis mutandis*, of other types of perception. Auditory perception, for example, can be data- or concept-driven and can be affected by the characteristic perceptual difficulties. In general, it is necessary to *interpret* incoming perceptual information according to rules that ideally can cope with all contingencies and not produce misleading or inaccurate results. These rules, used to supervise the perceptual process, are increasingly seen by cognitive researchers as relying on computational activity. (Hence Sloman, 1978, includes a chapter entitled 'Perception as a Computational Process'.)

Visual Systems

In animals (including human beings) vision is performed by the complex configurations of neurons in the brain, but it would be impossible to understand vision by talking solely about neuron firings and the activities at synaptic junctions. It is also necessary to consider vision as an exercise in information processing. Viewed in this way, it is possible to show that vision can be discussed in general terms that are equally applicable to biological and artificial systems. Hence we may ask: what computational tasks must a vision system perform?; what sequence of tasks is necessary for the complete task? (ie what is the algorithm?); and, finally, how might neurons or electronic circuits perform the necessary task sequence? An investigation of such questions is an important step towards providing robots and other appropriate computer-based systems with a visual capacity.

There are now many computer programs concerned with enabling artificial systems to see and recognise items in their environment (see Chapter 6 for an indication of work in this area). Already programs have been written or are being written to recognise a wide range of pictures and images: for example, cartoons, line drawings of three-dimensional scenes, photographs, 'stereo pairs' (to allow depth information to be derived), sequences of pictures showing moving objects, satellite photographs (giving

geological, meteorological or military information), and representations of 'impossible objects' (such as Escher's drawings). Some
of the programs exploit knowledge of how human beings perform
visual tasks, but some use rules that we cannot assume also govern
human visual activity. It has to be emphasised that existing vision
programs only model human vision in a very rudimentary way.
Human perception, unlike that (to date) in computer systems, is
affected by emotional preoccupation, a spectrum of (often confused) beliefs and expectations, degree of attentiveness, fatigue,
etc. Vision in simpler animals (eg insects) may be more closely
modelled by computer vision programs. At the same time, we
should not assume that computer-based perception need rely slav-
ishly on insights into animal processes. Animal faculties have
evolved in a particular environmental context: to meet machine
needs in a different environmental situation, it will often be useful
to try methods that are not discernible in the natural world.

Auditory and Other Systems

As with vision, there are both physiological and information-
processing aspects to the other sensory systems. (Vision has
received most attention from cognitive psychologists, roboticists
and other researchers because vision provides more information
for the system than do all the other sensory facilities taken
together.) Auditory systems are directly relevant to speech understanding in machines (see Chapter 7).

A wide range of touch ('tactile') systems have been developed
for modern robots (Chapter 9), and such facilities include sensitive
probes, responsive fingers and artificial skin. Some microcomputers now have screens that respond to touch, and we may expect
tactile systems to be more widely used in the years ahead.

The sense of smell, important to many biological species, has
been given relatively little attention by researchers in robotics.
One can imagine times when it would be useful for computer-
based systems to be able to detect molecules floating in the air.
Safety systems could well rely on being equipped to detect (smell?)
toxic gases, and some automatic fire-fighting systems need to sense
smoke when it appears. It has been known for many years that
different gases in the atmosphere can affect the conductivity prop-

erties in semiconductors, and this knowledge can be exploited in the design of practical sensor devices.

It has been suggested (eg by Masuda and Hasegawa, 1982) that, for robots to be flexible and adaptable in complex tasks, the individual sensors should be incorporated into a total system. This would obviously complicate the information-processing require- ments, but would also represent a closer analogy to what happens in human beings and other animals. Here again, insights into the cognitive processes taking place in the nervous systems of organ- isms could well help designers of integrated sensory facilities for robots and other computer-based systems.

MEMORY MECHANISMS

It has always been obvious that the storing of information is essential to all intelligent activity. And information has not only to be stored – on a short- or long-term basis – but also manipulated (processed) and retrieved when necessary. The cognitive approach to human psychology emphasises the crucial nature of memory mechanisms in biological and artificial systems. For example, the speedy retrieval of stored information is essential when a person or a computer needs to react in a rapidly changing situation. Or knowledge may be required months or years after it was first acquired. In fact all the cognitive tasks require that information be collected, stored and processed in various ways. Memory mechan- isms underpin all the intelligent operations in human beings and computer-based systems.

It has been pointed out, for example, that one factor that may be relevant to verbal ability (a type of intelligence) is how fast a person can search through long-term memory for particular items of information. This will involve a decoding process that will vary in speed of execution from one person to another. In fact, in connection with letter recognition (and other simple recognition tasks), a test of decoding processes in long-term memory has been developed by Posner et al (1969). The upshot of their approach is that the time needed to look up the name for letters in long-term memory – an important part of reading – equals the time for a name match minus the time for a physical match.

We do not need to pursue this matter (it is discussed in, for example, Mayer, 1981). The important point is that the cognitive approach to types of human intelligence (ie an approach based on information searches, information processing, memory usage, etc) can illuminate many traditional questions about human competence, and also pave the way for memory simulations in artificial systems. Other relevant considerations are such things as the holding capacity of, and the manipulation of information in, short-term memory. Hence a number of researchers (eg Earl Hunt and colleagues) have shown how an information-processing model can help to solve the long-standing problem of individual differences in mental ability. And this also illuminates difficulties in building artificial computer-based systems to perform cognitive tasks.

The reciprocal effect – ie AI illuminating aspects of human psychology – has been evident on many occasions. For example, work by Schank and others at Yale University has produced a theory of knowledge acquisition later vindicated by experiments on human beings. More recently it has been suggested that human memory is effectively 'restructured' when unforeseen circumstances are encountered, a strategy adopted as an adaptive mechanism. This idea needs to be tested to see whether it actually describes human psychological processes. Already Schank has produced programs that simulate human memory. These systems can store political information, news items, etc, restructuring their memories where necessary, and can then be experts with regard to the stored information, answering questions on the topics when asked. The success of such systems suggests that it can be profitable to consider human memory workings before beginning development of AI systems.

Various computer programs have been developed to model aspects of human memory activity. Thus in a model highlighted by Winograd (1975) the memory element comprises independent components controlled by a processing unit that calls up information when required and encodes specific input information to memory cells. Use is made of 'search' and 'active message processing', each memory element having the power 'to do its own computations on a message that is sent to the memory elements, and each element can decide independently what action it should take'. Such an arrangement is likely to exist in human memory, where specific items are linked with others in a network.

Sometimes, as with Reitman's (1970) Waiting-Room model, computer programs can be used to represent input processing in short-term memory. Here a close similarity is suggested between the relevant activities in computers and human beings. Other models – for example, Feigenbaum's EPAM (Elementary Perceiver and Memoriser) and Hintzman's SAL (Stimulus and Association Learner) – are regarded as representing limited subsets of human memory functions. EPAM, an early example of how a cognitive process can be effectively modelled, shows how a person can forget something for a long time but remember it when suitably prompted: items in memory may be hidden by other pieces of information.

The idea of limited-capacity processing in short-term human memory has also been suggested. Here efforts have also been made to develop the concept of a 'central executive processor', again extending the analogy between biological and artificial systems. Work on memory mechanisms, as with other areas of research, advances both the comprehension of human psychology and the scope for building AI systems. Expert systems, some of the most successful AI products, have been represented as enhancements to existing techniques for information retrieval. Again this illustrates how the handling of stored information is crucial to the realisation of intelligent machines.

LEARNING

Learning, intimately associated with the use of memory mechanisms, is essential to the adaptive behaviour of living and artificial systems (see Chapter 4). It has often been emphasised that much of the study of intelligent behaviour is necessarily focused on the ability to learn about the world, ie to store the results of experience. Lindsay and Norman (1977) point out that 'there is little formal distinction between learning and memory . . . the two are so interrelated that the study of one must necessarily be a study of the other'.

Cognitive theories of learning assume that experience involves the coding of incoming signals to allow memories to be built up and appropriate actions to be taken (here, 'experience' should be broadly interpreted to include all the ways in which new information can be presented to the system). Human beings can learn by being told, being shown, by doing, etc, and it should not be assumed that any of these methods is outside the scope of artificial systems. In a trivial sense, computer-based systems can learn by simply having new data fed into their stores; and they can also learn in a more autonomous fashion while performing an act (the much-cited Samuel draughts program learned to beat its creator on a regular basis, and there are other examples of this sort).

Ways of allowing artificial systems to learn can be closely modelled on how intelligent biological systems build up their memory stores in various circumstances. Again a cognitive approach to characteristic functions in human beings and other animals shows how analogous operations can be achieved by artefacts.

PROBLEM SOLVING

Problem solving, like memory and learning, is at the heart of much intelligent activity and can be found in such endeavours as language processing, computation, theorem proving, inference drawing and game playing. The character of the problem-solving behaviour varies according to the type of problem and the resources at the system's disposal (some systems are more intelligent than others). Broadly, ways of tackling a problem can be *algorithmic* (where a solution is guaranteed by following a defined set of rules or instructions) or *heuristic* (using empirical strategies akin to 'rules of thumb'). A *search* for a solution is attempted (see Chapter 4), the search strategy being adopted according to the problem and the scope of the system.

In human beings, problem-solving competence is constrained by various factors, eg limits on short-term memory and speed of information handling. At the same time we are able to access a remarkable body of information for various purposes. We may use pen or pencil to compensate for the limits on short-term memory, but this is often time-consuming and inefficient. Computers have some advantages in holding and processing information for problem-solving purposes, but such useful human talents as intuition, sudden inexplicable insight and 'quantum-leap' inspiration have not yet been computerised.

DECISION MAKING

Man has often been dubbed a 'reluctant decision-maker': choices often appear evenly balanced, and though the decision is important and has to be made it often requires a significant effort of will to 'take the plunge'. Decision making and problem solving are usually seen as interdependent. For example, at each stage in a problem-solving search a decision has to be taken.

It is often difficult to identify the reasons for a particular human choice. The decision may be influenced by mental factors of which the person is not consciously aware. Rules may be followed which are different to those that the person would recommend in tackling a decision-making task. Often the relevant information is partial or 'fuzzy' and, in such cases, likely to be interpreted differently by different people. (Efforts are now being made to enable computers to take decisions in conditions of 'fuzziness'.)

Human decision-making is also intimately connected with the perennially contentious issue of 'free will'. People are conventionally held to possess free will whereas machines, we are told, do not. In fact it is possible to show that there is no qualitative difference between human beings and computers in this regard. Human beings are programmed by the complex interaction of cultural pressure (including early upbringing, education, experience, etc) and genetic endowment; computers are programmed (mainly) by human beings. We do not need to pursue this controversial topic. It is enough to remark that just as human beings meet countless circumstances where decisions have to be taken so do computer programs contain numerous 'decision points', conditional jumps, etc, with 'if . . . then' instructions, GOTOs and the rest. It is useful, when designing artificial decision-making systems, to remember that the computer program can adequately model the choice mechanism in human beings.

OTHER MENTAL ATTRIBUTES

Many of the obvious mental activities of human beings – such processes as learning, remembering, problem solving, etc – are amenable to description within a cognitive framework. Other activities (such as having an intuition, dreaming, adopting an attitude, experiencing an emotion, etc) are less frequently discussed in cognitive terms. But we have seen that, for example, there are cognitive theories of emotion, and there is no reason in principle why other mental conditions and activities should not be discussed in terms of information processing.

The implications are clear. The development of cognitive psychology is extending the range of mental phenomena that can be modelled by computer programs (we already have computer programs to model Barry Goldwater, Tony Benn, psychiatrists, generals, neurotics, paranoics, etc). The inescapable corollary is that the scope for machine experience is constantly being enlarged. It is difficult to avoid the idea that in due course we will see computers that can not only learn and solve problems but that can also assume attitudes and experience emotions.

SUMMARY

This chapter has profiled the development of cognitive psychology, a development influenced by progress in computer science and itself mediating our views on computer potential. The reciprocal influence of modern psychology and artificial intelligence (a subclass of computer science) has been a constant theme. Computer developments encourage an information-processing interpretation of the human mind; new psychological theories suggest how mental attributes can be modelled in computer programs.

The interdependent nature of various psychological activities – learning, remembering, solving problems, taking decisions, etc – has been emphasised, and it is also suggested that other mental activities (intuition, dreaming, experiencing emotion, etc) are amenable to a cognitive interpretation. Finally it is proposed that just as an increasing range of mental phenomena are being modelled by computer programs, so we are enlarging the scope for machine experience.

Most current AI programs may be said to *mimic* aspects of human behaviour, but it should also be remembered that the development of a child begins with mimicry of older people in its environment. There comes a point when mimicry merges into actual duplication of aspects of behaviour: the child becomes autonomous, independent, mature. It is easy to build a scenario in which computer development is viewed in the same way (for example, Piaget's developmental psychology is directly rooted in the concept of information processing). Artificial intelligence, already a remarkable subset of computer science, has scarcely begun its evolution.

4 Problem Solving, Learning and Inference

INTRODUCTION

Artificial intelligence is concerned with a large and growing range of activities: collecting information, solving problems, taking decisions, playing games, reasoning, learning, proving theorems, perceiving (visual and aural understanding), language translation, writing stories and textual summaries, composing music, etc. This spectrum of interest accords well with what we know of *human* intelligence. Some writers have suggested that we should talk about *intelligences*, to highlight the multifarious nature of abilities in human beings. The craftsman, the footballer, the midwife, the novelist, the mountaineer, the physicist – all display examples of intelligence in achieving their objectives. What they have in common is a general cognitive competence, albeit focused in each case on a particular subject area. Sometimes we find that the competence is transferable, allowing the individual to cope well in an unfamiliar situation. In any event we can describe in general terms the elements that characterise intelligent behaviour, in whatever field it is manifested.

The individual perceives what may be termed a *problem* (broadly, a situation requiring action for an objective to be achieved); the problem is evaluated; then – using inference, stored information (*knowledge*) and/or other techniques and resources – the individual acts to achieve a satisfactory solution. Key elements in this situation – the use of memory, perception, searching for a problem-solving strategy, inference, etc – are central concerns of AI research. Some are considered in the present chapter, others later.

MEMORY MODELS

In human beings and other highly developed animals, memory is a complex and dynamic phenomenon. It can be long- or short-term; it can variously store words, numbers, tunes, shapes and other images and symbols; it can seemingly lose information or yield new unexpected connections and associations; and it is essential to problem-solving and learning activities. Many efforts have been made to produce computer programs that model aspects of memory. For example, Cohen and Feigenbaum (1982) describe EPAM (Elementary Perceiver and Memoriser), Quillian's Semantic Memory System, the HAM system, the ACT system, and the MEMOD system.

The EPAM system was developed in the 1950s and '60s by Edward Feigenbaum and Herbert Simon, and is now recognised as the first information-processing model of various human verbal-learning activities. The system, designed to rote learn nonsense material, has thrown light on aspects of short- and long-term memory. EPAM has explained such memory characteristics as retroactive inhibition, oscillation, forgetting, and stimulation-and-response generalisation*. The program is written in IPL-V, one of the first list-processing languages.

The system memorises nonsense syllables in serial lists or associate pairs. Typically a stimulus syllable (one of an associate pair) is presented to EPAM. The other syllable is then shown so that the association can be learnt (with a first presentation) or so that memory can be refreshed. The procedure is then repeated for each pair of syllables. The overall *trial* is repeated until EPAM can give the correct response syllable for each stimulus syllable. EPAM tries, in the performance mode, to produce responses to stimuli; and, in the learning mode, learns to associate stimuli and responses.

It is of particular interest that EPAM behaves much as a human

* *retroactive inhibition*: early learning adversely affected by later learning.
oscillation: learnt associations can be forgotten, to reappear later, and then disappear again.
generalisation: where similar stimuli are confused, responses may become interchanged.

in classical rote-learning experiments. Since the various types of behaviour – retroactive inhibition, generalisation, etc – can all be seen to derive from a single mechanism, the model is parsimonious (ie it nicely observes Occam's razor). Oscillation in EPAM helps to explain forgetting. Whereas it may be thought that information is permanently lost over time (by overwriting or decay), forgetting in EPAM occurs not because the information is destroyed but because access becomes temporarily impossible in the growing network of new associations.

Ross Quillian's Semantic Memory System is regarded as the first attempt to provide an operational representation of word meaning (computers need to know the meanings of words to perform machine translation, text summarising, speech understanding, etc). Here it is assumed that the *relationships* between words are sufficient to describe word meanings (this allows for different word *senses*, according to context). A distinction is made between *recognition* memory (which concerns Quillian) and *recall* memory (this latter involving knowing the full description of an item but not necessarily being able to recall its name).

A semantic network is built up using the concept of associative memory, an approach that facilitated the modelling of various aspects of human memory. For example, it was possible to establish a simple model of semantic ambiguity. A word may mean different things according to whether it is used as a noun or a verb, or a word may have different *senses* in different contexts. The Quillian model can find many of the senses of words.

This work has led to various developments in artificial intelligence. For example, the primary emphasis on linguistic knowledge has been generalised to other kinds of knowledge representation (see Chapter 5). In the area of psychology other associative models have been developed – in, for example, the computer simulation called HAM. This program, based on the associationist theory of Anderson and Bower, parses simple propositional sentences and stores the results in its memory. HAM was deliberately intended to have limited abilities – it can, for example, answer simple questions – so that it could model more effectively the essence of human long-term memory. (Anderson and Bower aimed to model the *strategy-free* component of long-term memory. It is suggested that specific memory strategies overlay a relatively simple mechanism that is characteristic of all memory performance.) The HAM model made a number of predictions that were subsequently tested by standard methods of cognitive psychology – to yield a voluminous literature.

John Anderson built the ACT system (as a general model of cognition) after his work on HAM (a model of human memory). ACT can perform various cognitive tasks. It includes, for instance, a short-term working memory of active concepts and also a production system that can effect changes in working memory and long-term memory. ACT, suggested by Anderson to be psychologically plausible, does in fact make reasonable predictions about experimentally-testable aspects of human behaviour. Hence ACT both expands our psychological insight and, by virtue of its *general* nature, provides an environment in which different types of psychological models can be built.

MEMOD, being developed by the LNR (Lindsay, Norman and Rumelhart) research group, is another ambitious general cognitive modelling system. The Group declared in 1975 that one system 'has to be capable of handling the representation and processing issues in syntactic and semantic analysis of language, in memory, perception, problem solving, reasoning, question answering, and in the acquisition of knowledge'. The MEMOD system began by representing linguistic knowledge but its authors were keen that it should be a *general* knowledge-representation system.

Even following this cursory glance at memory models it is obvious that memory cannot be considered in isolation from other topics of interest to AI researchers. Already we have mentioned linguistics, knowledge representation and general cognitive models (able to cope with perception, problem solving, reasoning, etc). The attempts to model aspects of memory quickly emphasised that a full understanding of memory would throw light on many types of mental processes.

PROBLEM SOLVING

General

Problem solving, like memory at the heart of much AI research, may be seen as a generalised activity that is relevant to many different types of process. The process of problem solving, in conjunction with *search* activity (see below), deals with inference, planning, commonsense, theorem proving, game playing, etc. Typical problem-solving tasks include:

— finding a proof for a geometrical theorem or a logical relation;

— finding the best move in a chess position;

— finding the transformations that will solve a symbolic integration problem;

— finding an optimum route between non-equidistant points;

— diagnosing a fault in an electrical circuit.

Such tasks are relatively easy to formalise, unlike the problem-solving processes involved in such human-focused fields as personal relationships, politics and education. In such areas we may not yet know how to quantify the various important factors, and even where a plausible theory is available it may be difficult to define the various factors in a way that allows a useful formalisation to be produced.

The simplest way to solve a problem is to use 'brute force', to thrash around until a solution is found. In computing, the brute-force approach relies upon faithful adherence to an exhaustive procedure that can be guaranteed to yield a solution. Speed of computation is also important if the solution is to be found within an acceptable time period: it is no use hitting upon a solution several seconds, hours or years after it was needed.

An obvious example of brute force thinking, in man or machine, is where every possibility in a set (a 'search space') is tested until the correct one is found. If there are many possibilities this approach can be very time-consuming, and it helpful to use appropriate strategies to reduce the size of the search space. Sometimes we may not know any such strategies, and brute force may be the only option – as, for example, with some approaches to cross-word puzzles and the testing of anti-cancer drugs. Problem-solving using computers may be regarded as developing intelligent strategies for reducing the search space so that a correct solution can be found using the minimum amount of computation. It may be possible to reduce the search space only so far, whereupon a brute force approach can then be adopted to assess the reduced number of possibilities.

In fact, brute force *without* a prior reduction of the search space is impractical for most problems that are worth solving. For example, the 'keys and boxes' puzzle (described by Boden, 1977) which can be solved by a program in 21 steps would take an average of 8000 years for a program relying on exhaustive search, even with one million decisions taken every second. A reduction of the search space can be achieved using a *heuristic*, a method that directs the problem-solving effort along the paths most likely to achieve a solution. It is worth exploring the heuristic/algorithmic distinction in more detail.

Algorithms, it is usually said, are bound to succeed; whereas heuristics, like 'rule of thumb', purchases economy of action by being fallible. But the heuristic approach can be *directed*, and so the simple distinction breaks down. A procedure may be algorithmic, in the sense that a solution is guaranteed, but certain heuristic search procedures are able to guarantee a solution – so such procedures are at the same time algorithmic and heuristic.

Heuristic programs tend to be flexible in their operation: there is, for instance, an effective postponement of decision making, the shape of the decisions being decided by the program itself in the actual operating circumstances. The simple algorithmic programs take decisions as specified, and circumstances in the world cannot influence the nature of the decision-making process. By contrast, a program such as HACKER can use experience to guide how it searches for information and what it does when it finds it. The heuristic approach essentially allows exploration of a search space in an efficient and economical way.

Most AI programs exploit the general principles of heuristic thinking, which we may also assume to operate, *mutatis mutandis*, in human problem-solving behaviour. Human beings have evolved a wide range of problem-solving ploys and stratagems, and many of these have been exposed by the cognitive psychologist. This allows for the structuring of equivalent heuristics into computer programs. (There is a common popular prejudice that computers rely solely on brute force methods. Were it so, artificial intelligence would be a much less exciting part of computer science.)

Planning

Many writers (eg Raphael, 1976; Cohen and Feigenbaum, 1982) emphasise the importance of effective *planning* before the actual problem-solving activity is initiated. Planning involves thinking about how the problem might be solved, after which the preconceived plan can be executed. It is easy to see that in such task domains as games, puzzles and mathematics, where all the facts are available in the description of the problem, correct planning will yield a straightforward execution. Where, by contrast, the information is incomplete, the execution phase itself will become more involved in intelligent problem-solving behaviour (this is so, for example, where intelligent robots interact with the real world).

Where comprehensive information was unavailable during the planning phase, progress can be monitored during execution, the resulting feedback being used to arrest fruitless behaviour before it wastes too much time or has damaging effects. For instance, a robot vehicle on a distant planet may find that its initial plan is inappropriate to unexpected aspects of the environment, so the plan should ideally be reformulated following the feedback of new information.

There are various approaches to the planning task: for example, hierarchical planning, script-based planning and opportunistic planning (discussed in Cohen and Feigenbaum, 1982). Again these approaches generally describe human, as well as machine, strategies in the evaluation of possibilities before the execution of problem-solving behaviour. It is often found that subproblems interact and complicate the task of limiting the search space. Subproblems interact when a problem has a conjunctive goal, ie when more than one condition has to be satisfied. Here a solution requires that the goals be achieved in the correct order, a circumstance that needs to be specified if the program is unable to infer the order from other information. Sometimes the initial plans violate the ordering constraints, and here it is necessary to go back and modify the plans so that a correct chronology is defined. The specifying of appropriate plans is directly influenced by the concept of search: what is the relevant search space, and what sort of search strategy should be adopted?

Search

Any attempt to solve a problem rests on the assumption that a solution is possible. In well-defined areas we can specify both why a solution can be found and how to find it. But there is nothing in the idea of a problem that logically entails the existence of a solution. Looking at the problems of human relationships, politics and war it is easy to imagine that there may be 'solutionless' problems.

The first task therefore is to satisfy ourselves that the solution to the problem lies in the places we intend to look, ie that the *search spaces* contain the solution. There is no point in developing intelligent programs to hunt endlessly for a non-existent solution. Alternatively the knowledge that a solution exists in a particular search space can be helpful in devising a planning and execution strategy. For example, it is easier to test new software on proven hardware, than to test new software and new hardware at the same time. In the former case, the problem of finding a fault is probably limited to the software search space; in the latter, the search space (software plus hardware) is larger, and at the start of the problem-solving procedure there are fewer constraints on the nature of the possible fault.

In mathematics some problems, but not all, can be solved. Often, where a problem cannot be solved, it is due to limitations on the competence of the mathematician. But to some mathematical problems there are *in principle* no solutions. In fact it has been proved that there are an infinite number of problems in higher mathematics that cannot be solved. This shows the futility of searching for solutions in the wrong space. We need to be sure that the solution exists in the space in question and that the space is not unduly large. If a solution exists, the larger the search space the more likely it is to contain the solution, and the less likely we are to find it.

The British Museum Algorithm (BMA) is sometimes cited as a 'worst case' example. If a horde of monkeys typed at random they would eventually reproduce all the books in the British Museum.

The process of trying to generate a particular word, or sentence or book by randomly generating combinations of letters, and watching for the desired one to appear, has thus been dubbed the British Museum Algorithm. Here it is assumed that the search space contains the solution and that the search procedure would eventually find it – but we would have to wait a long time. This is an obvious 'brute-force' approach.

The BMA approach can be proposed in many different circumstances, if only to show that we can usually think of better methods. Raphael (1976) considers the case of the man who has lost his spectacles. We could divide the surface of the world into six-inch squares, and then search each one, starting at the North Pole. The search space contains the solution and the procedure would find it, but it is not difficult to think of a better method.

Hence an important aim is to limit the search space to the smallest possible region that we are confident contains the solution. Then we can exploit our knowledge in an intelligent way to guide the search through the selected space. A *directed* search of this sort is more likely to produce an economical and successful result than is an arbitrary or random search. And a *systematic* approach ensures that options are not considered needlessly and that no options are ignored.

A key distinction made between search methods is that used to identify *depth-first* and *breadth-first* searches. In the former, the mind (or the program) follows its first ideas to their limits before turning to consider alternatives; in the latter, the mind skims the options and then selects one or two to examine in more detail. The differences can be understood by looking at a *tree structure*. Figure 4.1 shows a tree being explored using a depth-first search. At the various *nodes* the branches show the options that can be investigated.

In depth-first search the selected route is thoroughly explored, other options being ignored until a dead end is reached. At this stage the route is traced back to the nearest decision point and the next option is investigated. This approach can be used to best advantage where the tree is simple: otherwise much time may be lost before the solution, possibly represented at some distant node, is discovered.

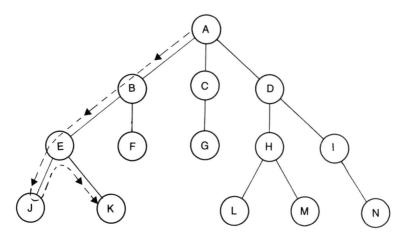

Figure 4.1   Depth-First Search

By contrast, breadth-first search (Figure 4.2) explores all nodes at a given level before pressing on down the tree. Again, with some kinds of trees, breadth-first search can be wasteful on time and other resources. Both depth-first and breadth-first methods are exhaustive enumeration techniques, totally unsuited to highly

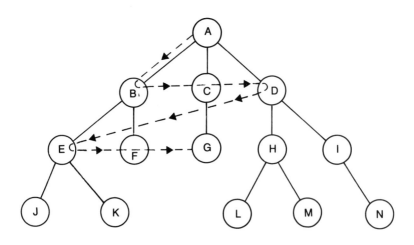

Figure 4.2   Breadth-First Search

complex tree structures. For example, it has been calculated that the number of situations (nodes) found at the bottom of the tree representing all possible chess moves would be in the order of 35^{100}. If each terminal node were investigated in a nanosecond, it would take 10^{138} years to find the optimum chess solution. Various search strategies have been evolved to facilitate a more economical use of time and effort.

Heuristic techniques can be used to overcome some of the problems of the brute force tree searching strategies. Two classes of heuristic techniques relevant to tree search are normally identified: *generator* functions which determine the order in which the nodes are visited (or, in some jargon, the order in which the tree is grown); and *evaluation* functions which influence the decision at a given node by supplying relevant information (eg information about the probable distance from the goal node). These functions can exert a powerful, and highly effective, influence on the search activity.

Heuristic search theory includes a mathematical proof that a heuristic using a numerical evaluation function (for example, like the one in the classic Samuel draughts-playing program) will necessarily find the shortest path to the goal, given certain relations between the goal node and the node at which the function is applied. Such a procedure is guaranteed to find the shortest path while avoiding an exhaustive search. In this way it is both algorithmic and heuristic.

There are various ways in which heuristic information can be applied in a search:

— to decide which node to expand next, instead of performing the expansions in a strictly breadth-first or depth-first way;

— to decide, in the course of expanding a node, which successor or successors to generate, instead of blindly producing all the successors at the same time;

— to decide that certain nodes should be discarded ('pruned') from the search tree.

It is useful, for example, to expand the node that seems most promising, ie to implement a 'best-first' (or 'ordered') search. This approach relies upon an evaluation function to estimate the promise of a node.

There are many techniques that can be applied in the search process. For example, 'hill climbing' uses a depth-first search approach plus a method for ordering the alternatives at each decision point. Movement proceeds through the option that offers the best improvement to the situation in a single step. Hill climbing has to cope with problems associated with 'foothills', 'ridges' and 'plateaus'.

Use can also be made of the 'branch-and-bound' strategy, AND/OR trees, combinations of breadth-first and depth-first strategies, bidirectional search, and such game-playing methods as 'mini-maxing' and 'alpha-beta pruning'. Mini-maxing, for instance, involves looking ahead in the search tree, the alpha-beta pruning method serving to reduce the number of moves that need to be scrutinised. (For details of these and other search techniques, see Barr and Feigenbaum, 1981, pp 46-108; Winston, 1979, pp 93-128; Raphael, 1976, pp 74-97.)

Hence search theory may be seen as concerned with the exploration and growing of *trees* and *graphs* (with a tree regarded as a special type of graph, having one top node and single predecessors for every other node, giving the inverted tree structure). The aim is to make a correct decision at each node so that the solution to the problem can be revealed in the minimum time. Nau (1983), for example, has developed a mathematical theory modelling the effects of search on the probability of making a correct decision. In essence, the search task consists in generating potential solutions and testing them. In artificial intelligence the computer creates symbolic expressions and modifies them sequentially until they satisfy the conditions for a solution. The systems display intelligence by selecting information from a problem domain and using that information to guide the search, ideally avoiding wrong turns and time-wasting explorations.

The GPS System

The General Problem Solver (GPS) was the first problem-solving program to separate its general problem-solving approach from the actual knowledge specific to a particular task. In other words,

GPS exhibited general abilities that could be applied to problems in various subject areas. From an AI point-of-view, this was an ambitious innovation. It has long been suggested that (human) intelligence is a *general* ability, relevant to coping with many different kinds of tasks.

GPS was developed from 1957 by Newell, Shaw and Simon, following the creation of the Logic Theorist program in 1956. The specified problem domain for the Logic Theorist was the proof of theorems taken from *Principia Mathematica* (by Russell and Whitehead). The Logic Theorist was able to prove 38 of the first 52 theorems in Chapter 2 of that landmark work. The program works by reasoning backwards from the theorem to be proved to other given theorems and stated axioms. It is not surprising that early versions of GPS, with this pedigree, were best suited to problem-solving in the domain of logic. In fact, despite the *general* ambitions of GPS it had, before the extensions to the program (Ernst and Newell, 1969), only solved two problems outside the logic domain. Ernst extended the range of problems that GPS could handle while maintaining its power at a constant level. This meant that the program could now fulfil one of the early intensions of modelling 'generality in problem solving'. The generalised program succeeded in solving problems in eleven different areas, including: the 'missionaries and cannibals' puzzle, mathematical integration, theorem-proving, parsing sentences, letter-series completion, etc. (It is ironic that theorem-proving in the propositional calculus of *Principia Mathematica* was outside the competence of the final versions of GPS, since it could no longer recognise the total number of times that a variable occurred in a logic expression.)

It is recognised that GPS could only solve very simple problems, its generality rendering it less efficient than the special-purpose problem solvers. If the problem demanded a lengthy search, GPS quickly ran out of available memory space on a machine with only 65K words. But GPS was not meant to have high-performance capabilities. Instead it provided, in the words of its authors, 'a series of lessons that give a more perfect view of the nature of problem solving and what is required to construct processes that accomplish it'. Additional capabilities, such as game-playing, were considered feasible as possible additions to GPS, but were never added. GPS, originally written in IPL-V, a list-processing language useful for modelling psychological phenomena, was the first program to incorporate a *planning* strategy for problem solving (see Planning, above), in which a simplified version of the problem is used as a model, details being filled in later.

The environment in which GPS solves problems has been called an *information processing system* (IPS), with the term *state* denoting what the IPS knows at a particular time. The knowledge in any one state is represented by *symbol structures*. One state can evolve from another by the application of *operators*. GPS searches for a solution to a problem by using operators to generate states, the final ('goal') state representing the knowledge of the IPS when the solution is found. The method of working is claimed to be a model of human problem-solving. For example, the *means-ends analysis* employed in GPS is reckoned to be commonly used by human beings in searching for solutions. It is not the only problem-solving strategy used by human beings, but GPS was never intended to model the whole spectrum of problem-solving activity in human beings.

TYPES OF LEARNING

Learning is one of the many activities that computers are supposed, by certain types of observers, not to be able to do. It is one of the intriguing contributions of AI research to have demonstrated that computers can not only learn but can do so in several different ways.

Many attempts have been made to categorise the types of learning found in human beings and other animals. One simple division of learning activity focuses on learning facts (knowing *that* . . .) and learning skills (knowing *how* . . .). Raphael (1976) identifies four categories of learning: *rote, parameter, method* and *concept.*

In *rote learning*, typical of computer systems, information is simply transferred into memory for recall when needed. It is commonplace for computers to contain lists of employees, inventory items, article references, or the symbols that occur in a program to be compiled. Samuel introduced a form of rote learning in his draughts program. When a position is first encountered, the program stores its description with an evaluation (ie which player is in the better position). The program looks ahead a few moves and makes a rough evaluation of the positions. In a future game, the program may notice, before making an evaluation, that the current position is one that was formerly memorised. The previous value is more accurate than one that would be obtained by a new evaluation, because it gives the result of previous additional look-ahead. Hence the rote-learned values help the program performance to improve game by game.

Parameter learning is best exemplified by pattern classification in computers. Categories are defined (eg using the idea of 'prototype' patterns), and the classification methods indicate how a new sample (eg a letter of the alphabet) should be assigned to a category. But letters, for example, may be indistinct, and it may be better to acquaint the computer with examples of such letters in the first place. The human expert, however, does not need to create a prototype from such examples: the computer is certainly well equipped to compute averages. So the human being presents the computer with examples and their classifications, and the computer learns how to classify future representatives of the same categories. (The Samuel program also contains a capacity for parameter learning.)

Method learning effectively occurs whenever a computer is given a new program. But can a computer learn a new method as a child might – accidentally or by being taught? In fact various programs can effectively learn in such ways. The STRIPS program, developed in 1969 at the Stanford Research Institute, was designed to control an experimental robot. Whenever STRIPS solves a problem it generalises the solution, by replacing constants by parameters, and stores the resulting plan. This means that whenever STRIPS finds a solution to a problem, it learns a method for solving a family of similar problems. In such a fashion, problem-solving and learning co-operate to facilitate the evolution of more intelligent computer systems.

Concept learning requires that a computer construct a new knowledge structure out of previously known concepts. For example, a program written by Patrick Winston at MIT in 1970, presented with a series of labelled examples, can work to generate fresh descriptions. In particular, the program was designed to learn about simple architectural arrangements. It can study a description of a picture, identify particular elements, offer descriptions (cube, wedge-shaped, lying, etc), and then determine such relationships as adjacency, support or connection. A graph structure can then be created and stored to represent all the characteristics, and the structure can be assigned the label provided by the human teacher to denote the complete assembly. The program can then consolidate a series of picture-structures to produce a single structure that represents the concept. For example, if the program is shown two (dissimilar) arches and several non-arches, it can ascertain whether other pictures contain arches. Hence the program can use given concepts to learn new concepts.

Early AI research into learning tried to generate self-organising systems that could adapt to their environments. For example, efforts were made to simulate evolution in the hope that new programs would emerge through random mutation and natural selection. However, such attempts failed to produce the types of systems that were envisaged and, in the 1960s, research shifted to other fields. With the emergence of expert systems in the 1970s there was a renewed interest in automatic learning systems.

Cohen and Feigenbaum (1982), sensitive to recent work on expert systems, identify four basic types of learning: by rote, by being told, by being given examples, and by discovering analogies. Again, as an example of rote learning the Samuel program is cited; programs that learn by being told include TEIRESIAS and FOO; the BASEBALL program learns from examples; and there is a sense in which the Winston program (1970) learns by analogy. In Boden (1977) we find a similar breakdown of methods of learning. Here there are learning by example (providing new knowledge of cues and models), learning by being told (new knowledge of facts), and learning by doing (new skills). Learning may consist in merely adding to a body of knowledge or in replacing old information by new (more accurate) information.

Programs have been developed to recognise physical objects in the environment. For example, a program developed by J. M. Tenenbaum can learn to recognise the door, table, floor, wall, etc in grey-scale photographs of his Stanford office. Two data structures – semantic and iconic – are used to represent the concepts learnt. Boden (1977) describes how an iconic data structure can interact with its semantic counterpart to produce a useful description of a tabletop. The Tenenbaum program can learn what something looks like, by being told that the item resembles something seen earlier or by way of example. To do this, it needs to be able to draw upon a large body of knowledge: for instance, it requires knowledge about colours, regions, surface orientations, etc. The implication is that learning in such a fashion requires a cognitive system able to construct, analyse and manipulate complex symbols.

Learning by being told may involve nothing more than passively accepting new information. It is possible, for example, to add new knowledge directly to a computer system, as when particular statements are added to the Belief Matrix of Colby's classic neurotic program. And other programs, with inferential ability, can produce conclusions that were not originally fed into the system. Where programs learn by doing, they exemplify one of the key criteria of an actual learning system – they use experience to improve performance. We have seen that the Samuel program is an example of this type of process. Sussman's HACKER program can learn general lessons from particular experiences in a world of simulated blocks.

In effect, HACKER learns by constructively criticising its own attempts to do something. Goldstein's MYCROFT program, complementary to HACKER, applies general knowledge of debugging to the specific domain of children's drawings – computers programmed by children produce drawings that are then corrected by MYCROFT. The program analyses the faults and helps the child to avoid them in future. Such programs directly influence our concepts of human learning and indicate, in turn, further ways in which computer systems can model human mental processes.

The HACKER program is a device for automatic programming: it is able to write and improve programs, and moreover it learns to perform better with practice. Automatic programming is a growing field likely to cause alarm in some areas. Will programmers be needed in the future, and how will we develop the 'windows' necessary to keep track of the complexities of particular programs? Sometimes the human reaction to automatic programming is alarmist ('Computers that learn could lead to disaster', *New Scientist*,

17/1/80). At the same time it is easy to see how learning programs could be useful in many kinds of circumstances. For example, Narendra and Mars (1983) have proposed how learning algorithms could be used in telephone traffic routeing.

Another practical reason for developing automatic learning systems is, as we have seen, the expanding interest in expert systems. At present, expert systems are given their knowledge by means of a laborious and time-consuming process. If artificial systems could learn more rapidly it would be easier to construct the knowledge bases without which expert systems are empty shells. It would of course be difficult for people to evaluate new knowledge in computers where this began to exceed the body of information held by human beings, Voysey (1984) has highlighted some aspects of the current debate, as revealed at the 1984 Paris Congress of the International Federation for Information Processing.

There are already many programs that are capable of learning in different ways, and their numbers will expand as increased investment is directed into research on expert systems (see Chapter 8). Already we have seen how learning is directly relevant to memory, problem solving, semantics and other topics of interest to the AI researcher.

GAME PLAYING

Game-playing programs have to be able to cope not only with the many revealed options as the game progresses but also with the fact that there are two competing players. There are many non-game human activities that exhibit game characteristics. For example, in business, politics, war, law and order, human relationships, etc there are problems to be solved by participants with conflicting interests. This suggests that a study of game theory is relevant to a wide range of problems in human society.

Hence the various problem-solving methods used by game-playing programs have to face difficulties posed by the game itself (ie illegal moves have to be avoided) and by the opponent (whose skill level may vary from one game to another and who may often act unpredictably). The various methods extend computer competence well beyond the constraints of brute-force searching. In chess, for example, computer programs have now notched up some impressive victories. Margaret Boden, writing in 1977, observed that the Greenblatt Chess Program was winning 80 per cent of its games among non-tournament players as well as a fair proportion of tournament matches. And in recent years some of the victories have been more spectacular.

A program that won the 1981 World Microcomputer Chess Championships was given a US Chess Federation league table rating of 1950, and chess programs soon began beating International Masters. In 1980 the North Western University's Chess 4.7 program defeated UK International Master, David Levy, in a tournament game, and in 1982 Chess Champion Mark V, marketed by SciSys, beat the UK Grandmaster John Nunn five times out of six. (The Mark V also found three correct solutions to the celebrated Zagorujko chess problem thought to have only one solution.) Andrew Page, manager of SciSys, has commented: 'There are certain areas of chess in which computers are already capable of deeper analysis than humans. The day of the unbeatable chess computer is fast approaching.'

Computer programs have also developed a high level of competence in other games: Go, bridge, poker, backgammon, etc (we have already met the Samuel draughts program). In one famous encounter, Hans Berliner's BKG 9-8 backgammon program, run on a DEC PDP10 at Carnegie-Mellon University, beat world champion Luigi Villa four times out of five. In such games as chess and backgammon it is obvious that the brightest computer programs far exceed the intellectual competence of the vast majority of human beings. (Computers are also writing their own chess programs. For example, the ID3 system has produced chess programs that are said to be five times more efficient than the best programs the computer's human master could achieve.)

Two of the most common methods used by game-playing programs are 'mini-maxing' and 'alpha-beta pruning'. In mini-maxing the aim is to select a move that will give oneself the best advantage and one's opponent the least advantage. This requires looking ahead in the search tree, a task that could become impractical with a complex tree if other techniques were not employed to reduce the scale of the search. The alpha-beta method, logically equivalent to a systematic mini-max procedure, is a means of cutting down the number of moves that need to be examined.

In the game tree each node represents a position in the game. The final ('terminal') nodes represent concluding positions that confer victory on one of the players. The various nonterminal nodes can be labelled with the name of the player who is to select a move at that position. If we consider a game in which A is to move and which has three moves (A-B-A) remaining in the game then the final nodes can be labelled (with 'win', 'lose' or 'draw') to signify their value to player A. Given the values of the terminal positions, the value of a nonterminal position can be evaluated by backing up from the final nodes, whereupon A can make an informed move. The evaluation assumes that B is also using a mini-max approach and that chances for sure wins are not overlooked.

The game tree can also be analysed from B's perspective. Here the nonterminal nodes are evaluated in a directly opposite way, and a proportion of the final nodes take on different values ('wins' and 'loses' are reversed, 'draws' stay the same). There are also game-tree representations that allow a single procedure to return optimal moves for both players.

The mini-max procedure can be fully defined (for either player or for both) when a complete game tree can be generated. Usually, however, this is quite impractical and it is necessary to use methods that yield satisfactory results when only a portion of the game tree has been explored. Often the exhaustive evaluation required by the mini-max procedure is a waste of time. Various methods have been developed to reduce the number of evaluations that need to be made. The alpha-beta technique (alpha-beta 'pruning') is one of the most common methods used for this purpose (see, for example, Barr and Feigenbaum, 1981, pp 88-93).

It is now recognised that the mini-max procedure and the related game-tree-search methods only relate to part of the game-solving problem. Such formal search methods need to be supplemented by other techniques that cannot be incorporated into a single numeric evaluation function. Detailed *knowledge* of a game can be used, for example, to supervise the ordering of look-ahead positions in order to assist the tree-pruning methods. We may expect such knowledge to increasingly influence the writing of programs for particular game-playing tasks.

TYPES OF REASONING

Reasoning is usually associated with problem solving: for example, the Logic Theorist used methods of deduction (reasoning) to solve problems connected with theorem proving. We will see that reasoning is a key activity in expert systems (Chapter 8) where the program is required to draw conclusions from empirical information. And reasoning can be of various types: deductive, inductive, analogical, commonsense, etc. The approach of Robinson (1965), for instance, is usually described in terms of *resolution* procedures (resolution being exploited as the basic rule of inference). This approach has had a major impact on commonsense reasoning and problem solving. It is suggested that the resolution approach may facilitate the building of a complete problem solver by describing problems in first-order logic (eg in the propositional calculus) and deducing solutions by means of a general proof procedure.

Again the early promise of deductive problem solvers was not fulfilled, and there was a shift away from the use of logic in commonsense reasoning and problem solving. Today, however, there is a revival of interest in deduction-based approaches to various activities associated with commonsense reasoning. Cohen and Feigenbaum (1982) have suggested that AI systems that reason with incomplete information are in fact equivalent to automatic-deduction systems. The problem with automatic deduction is the old 'combinatorial explosion' difficulty: with even a few parameters there are soon too many possible inferences to be drawn. Without domain-specific guidance it may be impossible to control the deductive process.

Most traditional discussion of automatic deduction has focused on classical first-order logic only (the sort of concepts and expressions found in the works of the nineteenth-century logicians and in *Principia Mathematica*). But now there is increasing awareness of higher-order and non-classical logics. There are, for instance, efforts to develop reasoning schemes that can handle partial or indistinct (ie 'fuzzy') information. It has been found that many of the representations in non-standard logics can be reformulated in logically-equivalent representations in classical first-order logic. This is fortunate since most of the well developed techniques for automatic deduction have been developed for classical first-order logic. (See Funt, 1983, for a recent discussion of analogical modes of reasoning.)

Another problem is that automatic-deduction techniques may not be well equipped to cope with *intensional operators* such as *believe* and *know*. Here semantics *and* true values are both important. Classical logic is regarded as purely *extensional*, since the truth value of an expression depends solely on the extensions of its subexpressions. Thus the logical OR is extensional because the truth of P OR Q depends only on the truth of P and the truth of Q. *Believe*, however, is intensional: the truth of A *believes* P depends on the meaning of P, not on its truth value.

Nonmonotonic logic, one of several nonstandard logics, has received much attention in recent years. In this connection, Marvin Minsky, for example, has emphasised that the treatment of commonsense reasoning as purely deductive ignores the ability to retract a conclusion in the light of new evidence. Here it can be seen that the set of inferable conclusions does not increase monotonically with the set of premises as happens in conventional deductive logics.

Much of the current interest in automatic deduction derives from the new attention being given to knowledge-based expert systems and their requirement for various logic-programming facilities. Logic programming is concerned with using high-level languages to write programs as sets of assertions. The assertions are regarded as descriptive statements about entities and relations. In particular, the assertions can be executed by an interpreter.

Logic programming has been used for a number of non-AI problems (eg database management), but it is of particular interest in AI because it offers a powerful alternative to LISP as an approach to symbol manipulation. Moreover logic programming is particularly useful for knowledge representation (Chapter 5), a key requirement in expert and other AI systems. Logic programming has been taken to characterise the specific programming style incorporated into the PROLOG language, of which there are now many dialects. In Europe, PROLOG is regarded as the major AI implementation language. It has also stimulated considerable interest in the U.S., and has heavily influenced the fifth-generation software research programmes in Japan.

SUMMARY

This chapter has profiled some of the central aims and activities in artificial intelligence. We have emphasised how different AI interests are increasingly interdependent: for example, research into memory models is relevant to problem solving, and this in turn is relevant to such activities as learning and game playing. Moreover, artificial intelligence is a progressive development: one success rapidly stimulates another. Increasingly we learn of intelligent machines equalling or surpassing human performance (the Mephisto III chess program has drawn a game with world champion Anatoly Karpov).

An indication has been given of some of the key activities in problem solving, game playing, etc (with reference provided to more detailed descriptions). Search trees, 'tree growing', 'tree pruning' and other processes have been introduced with attention to the place in the central AI concerns. Other AI interests – such as pattern recognition (Allport, 1980: *The basic mechanism of thought is seen as a process of pattern recognition*') – are considered in later chapters. One of the key AI topics is knowledge representation. If computers are to *think* using *knowledge* there must be ways of holding knowledge in computer memories. This requirement has led to the new field of Knowledge Engineering.

5 Knowledge Engineering

INTRODUCTION

Knowledge, in one form or another, is central to all AI activity. Today it is the intelligence of the computer system that transforms data and information into knowledge. Traditionally, *data* was seen as raw input, relatively crude and unformed; *information* was data that had been evaluated, put into a meaningful context. Now the *knowledge* level has been added. We might even say that *knowledge is information that the computer can think about.*

The use of the word 'knowledge' to signify the stored items that interest AI systems is no accident. Here the appellation of 'knowledge' is no metaphor: it signals the new circumstance that machines may be deemed to have mental states. When we say that a car 'knows how to corner' or 'doesn't like hot weather' we are using mental metaphors to denote properties of a nonmental machine. But when, in the context of expert and other AI systems, we talk of learning, acquiring knowledge and thinking we are beginning to use these concepts in a literal sense. Computers, we are finding, will soon be legitimately viewed as 'knowledgeable' and 'thoughtful'.

Any intelligent task performed by animal or machine requires appropriate knowledge. A particular problem (say, a chess position facing mate) may require detailed conceptual knowledge, or (say, selection of holiday reading matter) broad relevant ideas. This immediately suggests that different types or levels of knowledge are relevant to particular purposes. In geometric theorem-proving, for example, the system needs knowledge about position, shape, relationship, etc; for problems in genetics the system needs knowledge of Mendel's laws and of a method for computing combinations; and in medical diagnosis the system needs knowledge of how particular groups of symptoms are related to particular diseases. Different subject domains are associated with different bodies of knowledge: the human or computer expert is able to carry such knowledge and to think about it for problem-solving purposes.

It is also important to be able to estimate *how much* knowledge is needed to solve a particular task. If we know four relevant facts, is this sufficient? Or do we need to know four thousand? Winston (1979) has highlighted the 'one-two-three-infinity phenomenon' – once we perceive that a task is reasonably complicated, we imagine that it is immensely complicated. Appreciating how much knowledge is needed for a task is important for various reasons – not least because it facilitates a proper allocation of resources to knowledge acquisition, knowledge storing, etc. It also helps in defining the scale of a task: a problem may seem less daunting once we can say exactly how much knowledge we need in order to solve it.

Knowledge is represented in different ways according to the subject domain, the problem to be solved, etc. Some simple factual knowledge is held in simple tables or in more complex configurations. Other knowledge may be held as procedural rules specified as symbolic relationships. There are in fact many different ways of representing knowledge in an intelligent system (see Knowledge Representation, below), and it is up to the knowledge engineer to be aware of the various possibilities and to select the one most appropriate to the task in hand.

It has been emphasised that, in computer science, a good solution to a problem often depends upon a good representation. In artificial intelligence there are many representation possibilities, often with unclear criteria for a choice in particular circumstances. At the same time the choice of representation is critical for intelligent systems, because the representational features and the ways these can be exploited effectively define the scope for perception, understanding and knowledge in such systems. A number of questions arise in trying to design a representational philosophy for particular purposes. These are associated with the problems encountered in producing computer programs to use knowledge in an intelligent way to perform a task. We need to know, for example:

— how to build a representational system that avoids the ambiguity that tends to characterise human symbol systems;

— how to preserve flexibility so that currently unresolved details can be accommodated at a later time;

— how to recognise relevant knowledge (new knowledge may *become* relevant during the process);

— how to accumulate new knowledge (and to displace old knowledge that may be superseded);

— how to accept new knowledge when it is presented at an unexpected time or in an unexpected way.

Knowledge representation has been seen as the 'glue' that binds much of AI together. In fact AI activity is in part defined by the sorts of knowledge that are held in intelligent systems. Traditional data-processing systems tended to carry information of one particular type (eg statistical or other listings of quantified data). By contrast, AI systems need to store knowledge of objects, processes, relationships, etc; and sometimes such systems need to hold commonsense knowledge (often partial, fuzzy and hard-to-represent) about goals, motivation, time, intentions, actions, etc. Many difficulties are raised by the need to represent such a broad spectrum of knowledge.

First there is the task of structuring the explicit knowledge in a suitable form. Then there is the need to encode rules for manipulating the knowledge to infer new knowledge that is already contained, in some sense, in the knowledge base. The inferences and semantics have to be specified and controlled. And again, it is necessary to cope with new knowledge and incomplete knowledge. Underlying these various requirements is the need to develop methods of extracting the knowledge from a human expert in order to stock the knowledge base in the first place. This last is one of the key tasks of the knowledge engineer.

ROLE OF KNOWLEDGE ENGINEER

It is likely that the knowledge engineer has come to his new role via programming. There are various techniques of heuristic programming that indicate ways of collecting human expertise, and ultimately of making it available to others. Sometimes the task of capturing human knowledge can refine the expert's own expertise – by revealing inconsistencies in his own thinking.

An initial task of the knowledge engineer is to persuade the expert to submit to having his expertise translated into a form that can be stored in a data base. Often human vanity is at stake. Feigenbaum and McCorduck (1984) tell of the expert who gladly consented to have his knowledge mined, only to suffer a severe blow to his ego when it was shown that his expertise, gleaned over the years and for which he was well paid, 'could be expressed in a few hundred heuristics'. The individual was at first disbelieving, then depressed ('Eventually he departed his field, a chastened and moving figure in his bereavement'). And if experts are not worried by questions of vanity, they still tend to be busy people.

Once the expert has been persuaded to cooperate, the knowledge engineer immerses himself in the expert's field, finding out what the subject domain is all about, before embarking on a series of interviews with the expert. The knowledge engineer may use a tape recorder to collect the expert's replies to the many questions that will be put. The expert is first asked to describe what he does and to explain his approach to solving a relatively difficult problem in his subject area. If the problem is too difficult or ill-defined, taking the expert days or weeks to solve, then it would probably be unsuitable for engineering into an AI system.

Once the expert has provided a body of knowledge, it is handed over to the programmers who are required to produce the actual coding. There are various ways they could approach this task and it is up to the knowledge engineer to provide guidance. For example, it is necessary to decide which of several problem-solving frameworks ('inference procedures') best suits the specific subject domain. The programmers should aim to produce the first draft of the system as soon as possible, if only to maintain the interest of the expert. It is likely that there will be flaws in the first version and the involvement of the expert will be essential if things are to be improved. It is at this stage that inconsistencies in the expert's knowledge, or his superficial understanding of his own effective problem-solving methods, are likely to be exposed.

When the expert tries to improve (or refine) the knowledge that is given, the knowledge engineer should be particularly alert, sensitive to clues as to how the expert *actually* solves problems in contrast to how he *says* he solves them. It is the actual problem-solving methods that have to be enshrined in the eventual AI system, not the textbook descriptions of methods that may not work in the real world. Moreover the knowledge engineer is also trying to judge what the expert is providing, against the various knowledge representation tools that may be used: the knowledge engineer is constantly testing his model of the expert's activity, in the light of the information being provided by the expert. In this way the knowledge engineer can refine the advice he gives to the programmers producing subsequent versions of the system. Many problems can arise. The knowledge engineer and the expert are constantly shifting their points of view. At each stage of the process, refinements to the system will stimulate fresh thoughts, in turn encouraging program changes, and then further iterations of the cycle.

Feigenbaum and McCorduck (1984) have cited a set of heuristics, proposed by knowledge engineer H. Penny Nii, that are relevant in this field. In summary, these declare that:

— you can't be your own expert;

— the knowledge engineer must be prepared to throw away initial efforts (as does the writer or the painter);

— the problem must be well chosen (AI is still pretty limited in scope);

— you need to meet the expert more than halfway;

— use tools that work (build a new one if necessary);

— AI systems need weighting procedures to cope with uncertainty;

— AI systems need to be able to accommodate new knowledge, deleting material that is out-of-date;

— the problem needs to be interesting – to maintain interest.

The development of AI and other expert systems is a relatively new endeavour. The existing methods will evolve and new ones will emerge. AI systems themselves will increasingly contribute to the task of knowledge engineering. If knowledge engineering can be represented as an intelligent activity, then in due course artefacts will learn how to perform it. Already there is a requirement that certain types of AI systems explain their reasoning – to make it easier for human beings to evaluate the conclusions. But until AI systems are equipped to be knowledge engineers, the task of extracting human expertise and codifying it in a data base will remain painstaking and laborious.

KNOWLEDGE REPRESENTATION
General

In the earliest AI systems, knowledge representation did not have the status of a separate issue, though some 1960s systems recognised its general importance. For example, the SIR (Semantic Information Retrieval) system made use of Lisp property lists to represent and reason about information acquired from users; and the DEACON (Direct English Access and Control System) used ring structures to encode various types of knowledge. By 1970 knowledge representation had emerged as a separate topic for consideration. At this time, various researchers were considering what came to be known as *semantic network representation schemes* (see Semantic Networks, below), one of the most important current approaches to knowledge representatic important approaches include first-order logic, frames, and production systems (discussed below).

It is useful to regard a *representation of knowledge* as a combination of data structures and interpretive procedures which can enable a program to exhibit 'knowledgeable' behaviour. A central purpose of AI research is to develop the procedures which can intelligently manipulate the data structures. In this way a computer can think about its knowledge base. Such thought is part of the behaviour that effectively translates the data structures into knowledge, much as a human reader translates a book into a source of knowledge. How the procedures work on the data structures to produce inferences largely determines the competence (the level of intelligence) of the system. This is one of the reasons why knowledge representation is one of the most active areas of AI research today.

There are two broad categories of knowledge: namely, *knowing that* . . . and *knowing how to* . . .. The former is concerned with the storing of true propositions, the statements as to matters of fact. The latter relates to storing procedures and plans for action. In fact the two knowledge categories are closely linked: for example, facts can be used to facilitate knowledgeable behaviour (it is difficult to ascertain the possession of factual knowledge in the absence of a behavioural manifestation).

An AI system needs various types of knowledge in order to behave in an intelligent or knowledgeable fashion. The types of knowledge will depend upon the subject domain and the required behaviour, but typically will include:

— *knowledge of objects* (knowing that . . .), where facts about objects are stored;

— *knowledge of actions and events* (another version of knowing that . . .), where facts about events are stored;

— *knowledge about performance* (knowing how to . . .), where skills (how to ride a bicycle, swim, etc) are stored;

— *meta-knowledge,* involving knowledge about what we know (eg knowing the limitations on our knowledge).

It can be argued that these types of knowledge are not really distinct and that, if we allow they are, other types of knowledge should be included. This leads us directly into the age-old questions of epistemology (theory of knowledge) which are beyond the scope of this book. However it is worth remarking that, just as work on AI has illuminated many traditional cognitive concerns, so it has thrown new light on the traditional questions of epistemology (it is significant, for example that Sloman, 1978, in a book that is essentially about AI, makes frequent references to such philosophers as Kant, Hume and Descartes).

It is important to remember that the purpose of knowledge representation is to enable knowledge to be used in intelligent ways. For example, AI systems are supposed to be able to solve problems (in chess, military strategy, business planning, etc), to be able to control a robot (in the factory or on the moon), to be able to understand natural language (French, Russian, Japanese, etc) and to take appropriate action. The use of knowledge in such ways involves retrieving relevant facts from the knowledge base, and thinking about them, prior to the initiation of an appropriate programme of action.

Knowledge is first acquired and represented in some form. An AI system will typically *classify* a new data structure before it is added to the knowledge base: this makes it easier to use the knowledge, as required, in the future. On occasions, the acquisition of new knowledge can interfere with the established performance of tasks, and designers of knowledge-based systems need to be aware of this possibility.

Then the AI system may be required to think about its knowledge, reasoning from given (acquired) facts to new knowledge. We have already seen (Chapter 4) that there can be many different kinds of reasoning. Some of these may be summarised as:

— *formal reasoning* (as in mathematical logic), involving the manipulation of data structures according to the rules of inference;

— *procedural reasoning,* involving, for example, using a procedural model of arithmetic to solve an arithmetic problem;

— *analogical reasoning,* involving drawing conclusions about new cases by using established knowledge about other cases;

— *generalisation,* involving the generation of broad facts from sets of particular instances;

— *meta-level reasoning,* involving the use of knowledge about what you know.

Again we may emphasise that these types of reasoning are closely interrelated. In fact it is often possible to use formal methods to transpose a problem couched in one reasoning mode into a problem couched in another. But different types of reasoning are still more suitable for different types of problems, and the various reasoning modes require appropriate knowledge representations.

The various possible representations have various features that can be used to identify them. We may ask, for example, how much of the external world can be represented in a system and how much detail is needed by the inference procedures. Put another way, we need to know that the knowledge required by the system can be represented in the formalism adopted. And there are many different ways of encoding the particular items of knowledge, the facts, required by the system. Barr and Feigenbaum (1981) instance a simple fact – that robins have wings – to show that such an item can be represented in either of two semantic nets. One states directly that *wings are a part of all robins,* whereas the other relies on the relationship between *all robins are birds* and *all birds have wings.* We can see how alternative representations of this sort may be appropriate for different types of inferential purposes.

Other differences between representation methods relate to *modularity* (how easy is it to add to the knowledge base?), *explicit knowledge* (what knowledge in the system is accessible to the programmer and what knowledge is built-in, implicit, inaccessible?), and whether *declarative* or *procedural* methods are the most effective (this last question stimulated a 1970s debate which helped to emphasise the importance of knowledge representation in AI research). Some features of representation schemes are highlighted below *(Minsky's Frames* to *Semantic Networks).*

Knowledge, essential to modern AI systems, can be of various types and can be represented in various ways. To an extent, the various approaches to knowledge representation model the processes that take place in the human mind. It is worth remembering the reciprocal influences between artificial intelligence and human cognitive psychology. Before looking in more detail at the various representation formalisms it is worth glancing at how knowledge representation is accomplished in biological systems.

In Psychology

Knowledge representation mechanisms are important for human beings and other animals, as they are for AI systems. In biological systems, as in artefacts, knowledge representation is an important consideration for a variety of cognitive functions: use of memory, problem-solving, decision-taking, pattern recognition, etc. In human psychology the study of knowledge representation is often virtually synonymous with the study of memory. For example, one key memory representation, the semantic network, is central to a study of knowledge representation methods (see also Semantic Networks, below).

Before knowledge can be used it has to find its way into memory. This involves retaining a vast number of concepts (denoted by nouns, verbs, adjectives, etc) that can be retrieved at will. An initial point is that words are often defined in terms of other words – which suggests that the meaning of a concept is, in part, embedded in its relationships to other concepts in the memory. A concept, moreover, belongs to a *class* and exhibits characteristic *properties; examples* of the concept can be given. So much can be said about dictionary-type definitions.

It is also characteristic of concepts that they are *generic,* with a generic definition serving as a *prototype,* ie individual items (dogs, tables, nations, etc) need not fully conform to the generic definition. In memory representation, generic information about concepts provides general knowledge, allowing properties of the instances of the concept to be deduced but without insisting that particular instances of the concept be identical to the full set of generic properties. Such details are essential to an understanding of semantic networks in human beings and AI systems.

Memory modes may be defined as *semantic* (where circular definitions are used) or *episodic,* relating to 'particular *events* that have been experienced' (Lindsay and Norman, 1977). The latter is characteristic of an intelligent organism that can perceive the world in various ways, and of an AI system equipped with sensor devices to monitor changes in the environment. Both semantic and episodic memory can be contained in the same knowledge base, and we may expect semantic memory to derive initially from episodic experience. How this occurs in human beings is directly relevant to how AI systems might be enabled to carry out such logical processes as generalisation and abstraction.

It is clear that the knowledge base of memory can be used in many different ways. It can function as a semantic network in which nodes represent concepts and actions, with the relationships between the nodes creating an interconnected memory structure. Or the memory may be regarded as a collection of concepts, each being associated with a list of features.

Again it emerges that the work of cognitive psychologists, in exploring possible mechanisms of biological memory, points the way to how memory features – in particular, the representation of knowledge – can be structured into artificial systems. If a particular formalism enables an artefact to manipulate knowledge in a certain way, then it is conceivable that an analogue of the formalism operates in a similar fashion in human beings to facilitate similar results. It is one of the paradoxes of memory research that while human memory is little understood, effective formalisms are being developed to provide comprehensive memory facilities in artificial systems.

Minsky's Frames

It is convenient to describe a representation as a set of formalised conventions for describing things. The development of such conventions is highly critical to problem solving. One approach to generating an appropriate set of conventions depends upon the idea of a *frame,* a notion associated with a seminal 1974 paper by Marvin Minsky and a number of important recent developments in knowledge representation.

Minsky suggested that a useful way to organise a knowledge base was to break it into modular chunks, called frames. Individual frames may be regarded as data structures for representing stereotypical situations – such as making a cup of coffee or going to a birthday party. There are various types of information associated with each frame – about how to respond in the frame, about what will happen in various possible contingencies, etc. As with problem-solving tree networks, a frame can be seen as comprising a network of nodes and relations, though in this case the network has characteristic information-retrieval properties. The top levels of the network represent elements that are always true about the situation, whereas the lower-level have terminal nodes that must be filled with specific data. Related frames can be linked to form frame systems, important actions being mirrored by transformations between the frames of a system.

Frames defined in this way (also referred to as *schemata)* have expanded the idea of knowledge representation to develop AI techniques for such phenomena as computer vision and natural language understanding. The frame approach is powerful because the theory allows the inclusion of expectations and other kinds of presumptions. The terminals carry *default assignments,* so a frame may carry much information whose supposition is not specifically warranted by the situation. The default assignments can be displaced by new items that are more suitable to the current situation. They can thus serve as variables (or as cases for 'reasoning by example') or as 'textbook cases'. Semantic network representations have frame-type characteristics in some situations. (For a full description of the frame approach to knowledge representation see Minsky, 1974; Winston, 1979.)

Production Rules

Production system architectures are another influential method of representing knowledge in AI systems. These were originally proposed (for example, by A. Newell, 1973) as models of human reasoning. The production system approach is associated with the notion of a *rule,* each regarded as essentially a 'pattern —► action' pair operating on a store of relevant concepts. This notion has proved immensely useful in the manipulation of knowledge in expert systems (Chapter 8).

An AI system can accumulate knowledge in the form of production rules. This is useful because the knowledge in the specialist domain can be expanded incrementally, and can be expressed in a form that can easily be comprehended by an expert who is unacquainted with knowledge engineering. Effective rules are collected from the expert, checked for consistency, and then programmed into the AI system. Efforts are made at the same time to expose inadequate or inappropriate rules.

The rules comprising the knowledge base can have many different formats: the *if*-a-condition *then* an action format is common, with the *then* section able to represent inferences, assertions, probabilities, precepts, etc. One of several conditions associated with the rule determines whether the rule is potentially valid with respect to a prevailing model of the situation. A rule can require that a number of conditions be satisfied before an action (or inference, or conclusion, etc) follows, eg if a is the case, and conditions b and c are satisfied, then d is the case. Sometimes the final (inferred) state has an attached probability rating: for example, 0.7 may appear in the statement, signifying that there is a 7 out of 10 chance that the conclusion is true.

Rules can be handled in various types of system organisations; for example:

— *top-down,* where top-level goals are examined, and efforts made to match the right-hand side of rules to the goal. Where a match is found, components on the left are set up as further goals, and so on;

— *model-based,* where a model of the relevant world is used. Rules are used to establish and correct the model over time. This approach allows effective predictions to be made;

— *blackboard,* where the rules are organised into *knowledge sources* carrying expertise in particular subject domains. Here hypotheses can be established and modified.

Other possible system organisations for rule manipulation relate to methods for allowing computers to think in natural language, techniques for commonsense reasoning, and strategies for heuristic activity. Rule-based strategies are being exploited to enhance the competence of AI systems in general and expert systems in particular. (A detailed description of production systems and the associated rules, along with the various other knowledge-representation methods, is given in Barr and Feigenbaum, 1981.)

Logic and Programming

It first became evident in the 1960s that first-order logic could be employed as a knowledge-representation formalism, following work in automatic theorem-proving (see survey in Nilsson, 1971). We have already cited the interest in the resolution principle as an inference technique. Other research focused on recasting logical formalisms into computationally-oriented frameworks: examples here are the Planner formalism, the Strips planning paradigm, and the PROLOG programming language (this last important to the development of fifth-generation computer systems). There has been considerable discussion as to the merits of logic-based methods of knowledge representation.

Formal logic, developed since the time of Aristotle by philosophers and mathematicians, may be regarded as a classical approach to the representation of knowledge about the world. Statements such as 'all men are mortal' were recast in mathematical formulae which facilitated the analysis of formal relationships. This approach enabled conclusions derived from deduction to be guaranteed correct to an extent not yet reached in other representation schemes. Moreover, the use of logic-based representations have been popular in AI research since they provided a straightforward means of deriving new facts from old. Automated versions of theorem proving techniques have facilitated the development of programs that could establish the truth value of a new statement in a data base by attempting to prove it from the *existing* statements. When the number of facts becomes large there is the inevitable (and familiar) combinatorial explosion, and different validation methods have to be adopted.

Minsky and others have expressed doubts about the usefulness of classical logical-representation schemes to serve in all the various necessary complexities of machine and animal thought (aspects of this debate are well conveyed in Israel, 1983). Already the first-order classical logic scheme has been supplemented by a range of new formalisms. At this stage their respective merits are being debated and no single candidate has emerged as prime candidate for knowledge representation in AI systems.

PROLOG, used for logic programming, has been developed as a key language for AI and fifth-generation computers. This language uses the *resolution* principle, developed by Professor John Robinson of Syracuse University in the United States. Problems are solved by means of a series of logical inferences, much in the way that expert systems use deductive reasoning. The basic unit of a PROLOG program is a Horn clause which can either be a direct statement (or *assertion*) such as:

Fred works 38 hours a week

or an implication, such as:

if x works z hours *and* earns p/hour *then* x is paid y.

(The similarity to Production Rules, discussed above, is obvious.)

Such assertions and implications allow a specification to be produced of an information processing task or to define data base search requirements. In such a fashion the specification can function as a program procedure or as a relational data base enquiry. And formal techniques can be used to validate a PROLOG specification. PROLOG is easy to learn since it resembles the natural way of expressing problems.

Already there are many dialects of PROLOG for different purposes and for machines of different sizes. For example, the London-based LPA Ltd is offering PROLOG implementations for several microcomputers and for DEC VAX superminicomputers. Micro Prolog is offered for microcomputers configured around the Zilog Z80. At the London fifth-generation conference staged by SPL International, various successful PROLOG applications were cited. It has been suggested that PROLOG is a better AI language than LISP. Here we see the parallel development of new AI languages and of the associated knowledge representation techniques (see, for example, Dahl, 1983).

Commonsense and Fuzzy Logic

One of the central problems in AI is how to represent commonsense knowledge. This type of knowledge is not characterised by an easy formalism. Instead it relies upon rather shapeless categories, impressions, qualifications, probabilities, 'fuzziness', etc. Conventional knowledge-representation techniques – for example, using predicate calculus – are not well suited to representing commonsense knowledge. Traditional logic systems depend upon crisp, rather than fuzzy, concepts. Following the seminal work of Zadeh (1965), considerable work has been devoted to developing a theory of fuzzy logic that is applicable to the types of knowledge frequently found as an essential ingredient of commonsense.

Zadeh himself has contributed further, over the years, to the development of fuzzy set theory and related concepts. For example, a 1983 article, dealing with the representation of commonsense knowledge, uses the idea that commonsense propositions are *dispositions,* ie propositions with implied fuzzy quantifiers. Here fuzzy logic is seen as having two main components:

— a *translation system* for representing the meaning of propositions and other semantic entities. The system can be referred to as test-score semantics because it involves an aggregation of the test scores of elastic constraints induced by the semantic entity of the represented meaning;

— an *inferential system* for arriving at an answer to a question that relates to information in the knowledge base (further references are given to discussions of the inferential element in fuzzy logic).

It is concluded that a collection of dispositions is able to denote what is usually meant by commonsense knowledge. In particular this approach provides a computational framework that is relevant to managing uncertainty (a species of 'fuzziness') in knowledge bases, especially in the types of knowledge held in expert systems, whatever the actual subject domain.

Semantic Networks

These are frequently used in AI systems as formalisms for representing knowledge. There are many different types of semantic networks but they all share a common notation, comprising *nodes* and *arcs* (that link the nodes). The nodes (usually drawn as circles or boxes) represent *objects, concepts* or *situations* in a particular domain, and the arcs represent the *relations* between the nodes. As with other devices in AI, semantic networks can represent both psychological models of memory and functional representations for artificial systems.

A simple semantic representation of, say, *all women are people* could be given using two nodes and a linking arc (labelled isa, 'is an example of'):

If we wanted to talk about a particular woman the representation could be extended to:

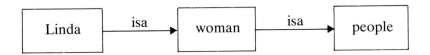

This type of representation makes it easy to achieve valid deductions simply by following the arrows. The ease with which such deductions can be made about *inheritance hierarchies* is one of the reasons for the popularity of semantic networks.

The above representation can be further extended by including another type of link to signify possession of a property

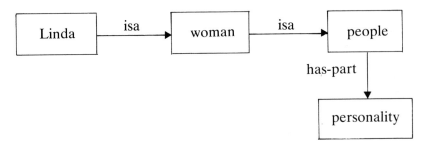

This signals that people have personalities, and so we can already deduce that this is one of Linda's characteristics. Semantic networks can be extended in this way to represent complex relationships between objects, actions, etc, and to signify concepts such as 'properties of', 'owned by', etc (see, for example, the detailed discussion of semantic networks, largely from a psychological point of view, in Lindsay and Norman, 1977, pp 386-411).

There is no single idea of what a given representational structure means, as there is in classical logic. A particular network acquires meaning according to the nature of the procedures that manipulate the network. Many different procedures have been developed for making inferences, and these are applicable to a wide range of tasks involving knowledge manipulation. Semantic networks, of whatever type, are seen as a popular representation scheme in AI: they aid the central AI task of symbolic computation and also efforts to understand phenomena such as association in the psychology of memory.

Learning Systems

Any learning system, biological or artificial, is concerned with the acquisition of knowledge and its storage using one representation or another. Various problems arise during the learning process: what, for example, is the effect of new knowledge on knowledge that is already stored? The way knowledge is stored directly affects how learning takes place and indeed whether it takes place at all. If, for example, a system uses *evaluation functions* to control a search, then learning will involve acquiring better evaluation functions; but if *production rules* are used, then learning will involve the generation of new rules that are capable of organising new types of behaviour. Langley (1983) has profiled some of the representation considerations involved in the development of effective learning systems. Here it is emphasised that input must be carefully crafted before successful learning can occur. Systems that could learn using different types of knowledge representations would obviously be desirable but such a possibility lies in the future.

SYSTEM FEATURES

Knowledge representation is one of the central research interests in artificial intelligence. Work is currently being conducted on a variety of systems (for problem-solving, learning, etc) to illuminate knowledge manipulation difficulties and to develop more effective representation strategies. Here we briefly draw attention to a few such systems (usefully profiled in *Computer,* October 1983):

> The Procedural Semantic Networks (PSN) project was begun in 1976 at the University of Toronto. PSN is seen as an attempt to integrate semantic network and procedural notions. The knowledge base comprises *objects, tokens, links,* etc (Mylopoulos et al, 1983). Two large knowledge-based systems, both developed at the University of Toronto,

use PSN as a knowledge representation language: the Alven system and the CAA system.

The Krypton system is an experimental knowledge-representation project that distinguishes between definitional and factual information by exploiting the features of both frame-based and logic-based languages. The result is a system that is defined in functional rather than structural terms. Krypton is now being implemented in Interlisp-D. Brachman et al (1983) give a detailed description of Krypton characteristics and how the system is constructed. Preliminary discussion focuses on features of frame-based languages.

The KL-One system uses a representation approach in which each concept (relating to objects, times, places, conditions, functions, etc) can be characterised as a configuration of attributes or parts, satisfying certain restrictions and standing in specified relationships to each other. The concept of a *structured taxonomy* is used (Woods, 1983). This is seen to have implications for programming and other system implications.

The Sage system is a production system that learns heuristics from experience. The program is presented with initial and goal states, and rules to control the search for a solution to the problem. Sage is closely related to the Lex system which also learns search heuristics from solution paths. Langley (1983) describes the Sage system with attention to the modularity of rules and data, semantically equivalent rules, etc.

The Bacon system (also in Langley, 1983) is being developed at The Robotics Institute to discover empirical laws. Provided with observations, the system notes relations between variables, postulates properties and arrives at a law. Again representation considerations are important in determining, for example, how narrowly the data needs to be tailored.

The various knowledge-based systems rely directly on specific representation formalisms. The representations adopted for systems design determine the scope and effectiveness of the systems, and influence the selection of appropriate subject domains for systems development.

SUMMARY

This chapter has highlighted the central importance of knowledge and knowledge-representation to AI systems. The significance of these considerations has been advertised by the frequently-observed, and not always helpful, habit in the literature of treating expert systems and knowledge-based systems as synonymous. The new interest in knowledge engineering emphasises the relevance of cognitive psychology to current AI research (*knowledge* is a psychological concept).

The work of the knowledge engineer has been briefly profiled, and some indication given of the sorts of topics that occupy the attention of researchers into representation formalisms. We have seen that there are many, often overlapping, approaches to knowledge representation – first-order logic, fuzzy logic, semantic networks, frames, production systems, etc – and that these allow the building of various classes of AI systems of differing complexity and for different purposes.

It has also been emphasised that knowledge representation can be considered in isolation from other AI concerns. It is intimately involved with research into learning systems, problem solving, game-playing, etc. Again we see the interlocking character of the various problems studied by the AI researcher.

6 Visual Perception

INTRODUCTION

Wherever intelligence exists, there is both an internal ('cerebral') element and a behavioural element. The most competent thinking capability is of no use unless it yields behavioural consequences. With computers the behavioural element may consist in nothing more than a screen display showing the results of computation: the display is a means of broadcasting the answer to a query, the solution to a problem, a decision that is taken, etc. It is akin to a person, having thought about a problem, writing down the solution or telling another person what he has decided. Of course computers too can produce printout or speak their conclusions.

Such behaviour – generation of displays, production of printout, speaking, etc – represents, on the output side, how an intelligent system maintains contact with the outside world. The 'outside world' for computers largely consists of the human beings who use the computer systems, so computer output is produced in forms that are intended to be comprehensible to people. Increasingly, efforts are being made – as, for example, with computers having an interactive dialogue capability – to adapt computer behaviour to human psychological requirements (ie to make computers 'user-friendly').

It is also required that computer systems maintain contact with the outside world by coping with incoming information in various ways. Traditionally this information is presented to the computer in a form that the system can understand. This means that formats, codes, standards, etc have to be imposed on information presented to a computer. It cannot sort out incoming information unless the information is submitted in a well defined fashion, via a keyboard, magnetic disks, etc. But this traditional computer requirement has represented a severe limitation on the capacity of a computer-based system to respond to events in the real world. Human beings can detect objects and events by means of sensory systems, ie sensors of various types linked to dedicated information-processing centres in the brain. These facilities enable a person to, for example, *see* what is going on without having to wait for a laborious prior translating of visual data so that the brain can then make sense of it. Of course an effective translation takes place – but very rapidly, in the brain, and in conjunction with other relevant information-processing activity.

The immense value of sight to biological systems striving to achieve particular objectives in the real world has long been obvious. It is significant that there is no highly-evolved biological species on earth without sophisticated vision (except for a few subterranean species where the absence of light renders sight rudimentary). Computer-based systems would obviously be more effective if they could see, hear, etc, ie rapidly translate available sensory information into forms that could be used to organise useful and purposeful behaviour. Already we are witnessing the emergence of *seeing robots* in factories and other environments, and tasks such as mechanical inspection are today being efficiently carried out by machines equipped with artificial vision.

The programming of computers to interpret visual data, ie to see, is one of the central research and development provinces of artificial intelligence. Here there are many theoretical interests (development of suitable computational algorithms, pattern recognition, scene analysis, component identification, etc) and various commercial pressures. It is clear, for instance, that an increasing range of factory tasks will be carried out by automated systems with a vision capability. Research into such systems will be influenced by what we know of the faculty of sight in biological organisms.

THE BIOLOGY OF VISION

One impact of computer science on cognitive psychology is that we find it increasingly useful to talk about *programs for seeing*, a phrase that neatly links the computing and biological worlds. The programs, whether in artefacts or animals, must have the power to interpret incoming information so that the system (of which the programs are a part) is provided with a picture of the outside world. What happens, for example, when someone sees a red object? There is an almost instant impression of immediacy though neither the object nor a bunch of red light has floated up the optic nerve. What has happened is that the object has reflected (or emitted) light of a certain frequency, which then causes photo-chemical changes to occur in the retina, resulting in appropriate neural impulses to be fed down the optic nerve to the sight centres in the brain. There is some sense in which the nerve impulses are *symbols* representing the red object and which can be decoded by an appropriate information-processing mechanism (brain or computer).

The typical human eye contains a retina comprising a mosaic of millions of rods and cones, each of which detects a tiny part of an image thrown on it by the lens. This causes minute electrical and chemical changes involving both analogue and digital computation. Many of the nerve cells in the retina do not simply generate binary yes-or-no responses but produce graded changes which then combine to influence the binary responses from larger cells in the vicinity. It is interesting that some cave-living creatures have skins that are sensitive to light: when light falls on the skin of certain species of cave fish, the creatures are induced to swim until they are again happily in the dark. Here the light-sensitive skin generates nerve impulses that effectively *symbolise* the presence of light and which are *decoded* by the brain to produce swimming actions. In mammals, particularly man, the symbolising and decoding processes are much more complex: a vast range of objects and events can be recognised and interpreted to stimulate a host of appropriate (and sometimes inappropriate) actions. We already have light-seeking and light-avoiding robots but there are no computer programs that provide machines with a visual competence anything like that to be found in the normal human being.

The neural pathways carry information from the eye to at least three parts of the brain – the midbrain, the cerebellum, and, via the thalamus, to the cortex. All these parts are involved in any act of vision, with the midbrain and cerebellum concerned largely with detailed control of eye movements and the cortex concerned with the more detailed analysis and interpretation of incoming signals. The cortex is an immensely complex folded layer of nerve cells arranged in columns, fed by a pattern (or map) of nerve fibres which exactly reproduces the pattern of receptor cells on the surface of the retina. There are similar cortical maps for hearing and for touch though, interestingly enough, not for smell or taste (which cannot detect shape). The visual cortex itself may be regarded as a greatly expanded version of the retina, there being hundreds of cortical cells for every single retinal receptor.

The columns of nerve cells are each sensitive to some particular features: for example, a line set at 10 degrees to the horizontal, or a particular colour. The myriad of codes for lines, colours, etc are laid down in cell organisation by hereditary but may be refined by use. The signals passing through the various visual areas are decoded and combined in many different ways to give the organism a picture of what is being seen. At the same time the brain is pursuing an active search for other data that is relevant to the goal in hand.

We may assume that there are substantial differences between the processes used by biological systems to provide a vision capability and the analogous processes being developed for machines. The nerve cells in the retina and the cerebral cortex rely upon both chemical and electrical effects, whereas silicon circuits have little interest in chemistry. Connections between neurons are very numerous and are usually distributed in three dimensions. There are far fewer connections between electronic components in digital computers, and these are largely laid out in two-dimensional structures. But though the respective hardwares of biology and computers differ greatly it is likely that there are similar computational events in the different types of systems. This should not surprise us. There are advantages to computer designers in following computational routes already mapped out by biological systems for analogous purposes. Vision in human beings is a remarkable phenomenon: if we can even begin to emulate some of its key processes we are well on the way to understanding how artificial sight may be built into machines.

THE COMPUTATIONAL ASPECT

We have emphasised that vision is more than a matter of hardware. It is also an algorithmic question (what sequence of steps is required to complete a visual act?) and a computational question (what computational tasks are the algorithms required to accomplish?). Of course these questions are very interdependent. An elegant and effective algorithm is useless if the hardware (circuits or cells) cannot cope with it; and it is possible that different algorithms – required for different aspects of the sight process, and individually practical – cannot co-exist in the same hardware structure. Efforts have been made to develop the individual algorithms needed to compute the various elements that combine to produce the full sight act (eg seeing a red MG motor car and knowing what it is). Poggio (1984), for example, explores a sequence of algorithms that:

— extract information (edges or pronounced contours in the intensity of light) from visual images;

— and then calculate from those edges the depths of objects in the three-dimensional world.

Here there is particular reference to *stereopsis*, the familiar phenomenon of stereo vision, which has been researched at the Artificial Intelligence Laboratory of the Massachusetts Institute of Technology and elsewhere. It may be pointed out that stereopsis – like other physiopsychological processes, a seemingly simple affair – has proved difficult to build into automatic systems, even though much relevant empirical evidence about the phenomenon is available.

Light is reflected (or emitted) from the three-dimensional world onto the two-dimensional retinal array. In AI research, solid-state electronic sensors can carry out the analogous functions to those performed by the rod and cone receptors in the human retina. At MIT, for instance, such sensors produce an array of 1000 by 1000 light-intensity values, with each value a *pixel* (or picture element). It is obvious that several computational processes have to be carried out on the information provided by the two-dimensional (receptor or cell) array before an accurate picture of the external world can be constructed. Various processes (*modules*) work in parallel and in series to build up the various aspects of the required picture. For example, several vision modules are necessary to construct an image of the three-dimensional geometry of the world. Other modules are necessary to cope with deriving shape from shading, from motion, from occlusions, etc, and from the information supplied from stereopsis. Initial processing takes place on the raw image (the sensitivity response of the retina or of the sensor array), but other modules may prefer to work on later images (ie images generated by prior computation).

In animals with binocular vision, each eye views the world from a slightly different angle. This means that the brain is provided with information (about a scene, for example) that is disparate but pertinent. Stereopsis relies on decoding the disparities to achieve an effective representation of three-dimensionality. This involves more than a simple exercise in trigonometry, though trigonometrical processes can be involved at various stages of the computation. In fact, stereopsis relies on four procedural steps: select space location from one retinal image; identify the same location in the other retinal image; measure their positions; from the disparity between the two measurements calculate the distance to the location.

The first two steps (ie finding the projection of the same point in the physical world in each eye) are highly problematical. How, for instance, are two two-dimensional arrays of cells to be matched, point by point? Work by Bela Julesz at AT & T Bell Laboratories on random-dot stereograms has helped researchers to formulate the computational goal of stereopsis. It is necessary to match elements in the two images without being able to rely on the recognition of objects or their parts. The brain achieves this task by making assumptions about the physical world that usefully constrain the problem. David Marr and Tomasco Poggio, working at MIT in 1976, found that simple assumptions about physical surfaces (eg that variation in depth over a surface is only discontinuous at a boundary) could render the problem manageable by stereopsis algorithms that could be performed by a computer. This finding led to further insights into stereopsis: for example, about the relevance of intensity to image interpretation.

Poggio (1984) comments that 'a combination of computational

arguments and biological data suggests that an important first step for stereopsis and other visual processes is the detection and marking of changes in intensity in an image at different spatial scales'. The execution of the Marr/Poggio stereopsis algorithm involves performing a series of calculations, which means that a computer can perform one of the central procedures required by a typical visual act. Attention may also be drawn to a theoretical extension and computer implementation of the algorithm by Grimson at MIT. This development is relevant to, for example, the analysis of aerial photographs, and to the effective mimicry of many of the properties of human depth perception using sight.

Another consequence of this type of research is that the importance of prior knowledge is emphasised. In short, what we know determines what we see (or hear, etc). This has many implications for the design of AI systems, and there is a reciprocal influence: progress in computer science affects our view of human perception (for example, research on computer programs that interpret pictures shows how perception uses knowledge and expertise). Again it is clear that very complex computational procedures are necessary for what appear to be simple perceptual activities. Even recognising a simple item in the field of view depends upon such tasks as:

— discerning points of differing intensity;

— deciding how to group particular features;

— deciding which features to ignore;

— deciding which contiguous elements are not related;

— making inferences about hidden parts of objects;

— using awareness of apparent inconsistencies to redirect attention to acquire new data;

— recognising clues as to the *type* of scene, in order to discriminate between different interpretations that are all supported by the available evidence;

— recognising that simple and seemingly self-evident interpretation may in fact be erroneous.

Different types of computations are required by these and other related processes that are important to simple acts of sight (eg seeing and recognising a line as a line). Prior knowledge (ie pre-programmed structures) is essential to the performance of the various tasks that underlie sight and other examples of perceptual behaviour (Sloman, 1978, has engagingly drawn attention to how Emmanuel Kant, in the eighteenth century knowing nothing about computer science, posited the necessity of prior knowledge to human cognitive abilities).

It is clear that vision requires a complex of co-operating computational processes, and that it is possible to model a number of these in artificial systems. Perhaps AI systems will evolve methods that are unknown in biological systems but, bearing in mind the superlative efficiency of the human sight faculty, we are likely to benefit AI development most by deepening our understanding of existing biological vision systems.

TOWARDS ARTIFICIAL VISION

General

Vision can be represented as the information-processing task of understanding a scene from its projected images, a definition that immediately suggests that computers can be used for the task. An image has been defined as a two-dimensional function $f(x,y)$ obtained with a sensing device that records the values of image features at all points (x,y). Here the values can be represented by binary terms (for black-and-white images), by gray level (for half-tone images), or by vectors of colour measures (for colour images). An array of *pixels* (small picture elements) is used to represent the image by facilitating the measurement of values at each pixel position. Computer vision systems are required to understand the scene depicted by arrays of pixels. Cohen and Feigenbaum (1982) have identified three broad classes of computer-vision activities:

— *signal processing*, where an input image is transformed into another image that has more useful properties. This type of activity is commonly termed *image processing* or *picture processing*;

— *classification*, where images are grouped into predetermined categories. Feature values may be extracted from images, statistical decision methods being used to determine how closely an image fits a class. This type of process is often called *pattern classification* (or *pattern recognition*, for historical reasons);

— *understanding*, where a description is constructed of both the image and the scene it depicts. *Scene analysis* is often used to distinguish between processing two-dimensional images and three-dimensional scenes.

There is an effective hierarchy of concerns in vision research. For example, *low-level vision* (or *early processing*) aims to extract primitive features (eg intensity changes, edge orientations) from an intensity array. Lines, regions, shapes, etc are then extracted by higher-level processing (at this level often termed *segmentation* or *intermediate-level processing*). *High-level vision processing* deals with complete objects and, using domain-specific knowledge, aims to construct descriptions of scenes.

Picture Processing

Ideally a computer-based vision system should be able to recognise any object in its three-dimensional environment, and in fact this is very much the aim of current research. However, a preliminary task which can later be enhanced is for a computer vision system to recognise two-dimensional pictures of various types. It is useful to explore the various ways in which pictures can vary and be compared.

Pictures can be simple (eg a drawing with few lines) or complex (eg a photomicrograph of a living cell). The picture content may be a literal representation or an impression, a caricature, an abstract interpretation. And when the picture is placed in the computer, using analogue-to-digital conversion methods, information may be lost, particularly where the picture contains subtleties of shadows, reflections, obscured items, distortions due to perspective, etc. These variations and complexities make it difficult to construct a computer system that can cope with all contingencies.

The AI researcher can select the type of picture that best advances his work, whereas a biochemist or an astronomer is forced to deal with specific types of illustrations, namely those photographs and other illustrations that relate directly to their particular fields of interest. Having selected a type of diagram or photograph, the AI worker may be confronted with the problem of *rendition*: for example, in character-recognition systems the central task is to identify all renditions as equivalent (eg to be able to recognise all versions of the same alphabetic letters, whatever the typeface). The accuracy of a rendition also bears on this problem: the difficulties are compounded if parts of a picture are missing or obscured. Nonetheless, an adequate computer-vision system should be able to handle a wide range of representations, even if some of them are far from perfect. The usual procedure is to regard the picture as comprising a large number of picture points ('pixels') which can take on various values (or degrees of intensity) according to the picture of which they form a part.

In *template matching*, a common form of two-dimensional figure identification, it is necessary to determine the degree of match between the defined template and the sample figure being examined. In a simple case the computer adds up the number of array positions in which the template and the sample agree. However, misalignment of the sample can result in serious errors. Moreover any given template is useful for identifying only one defined shape, and some shapes (eg triangles) are capable of infinite variations. Thus a computer that can recognise such shapes must have access to more than simple template/sample matching programs. In fact there are many programs that are equipped to find and count lines, to find and analyse corners, to follow planes and contours, and to count relevant objects in a scene (see below).

The Blocks World

For more than a decade, AI researchers have explored ways of enabling computers to recognise and interpret simple scenes involving randomly positioned blocks of different sizes. Several computer programs (see Vision Programs, below) have become famous because of their capacity to function with seeming intelligence in specific blocks worlds. The blocks approach is useful because it represents an effective simplification of the real world. It facilitates the development of techniques for recognising straight lines, corners, etc, which can be enhanced for recognition of more complex scenes. At the same time it is recognised that the blocks worlds are so constrained that the associated image-understanding procedures cannot be generalised for application to the real world. All computer-vision systems make assumptions to constrain the particular environments for ease of handling. It is helpful, as with the blocks worlds, when the assumptions are made explicit.

Consider the example of a television camera viewing an array of blocks. The image is digitised and held in the computer's memory as an array of numbers representing the intensities of the particular picture points. Before the computer can begin to interpret the array of numbers it is necessary, using various smoothing and sharpening procedures, to 'improve' the information held in the memory (for example, 'noise' has inevitably affected the accuracy of the picture). Various methods and rules can be adopted to achieve the necessary improvement: for instance, if a picture point is brighter than its eight immediate neighbours then its value can be reduced, and inappropriate dimness can be similarly modified. At the same time, care should be taken to ensure that adjustments of this type do not significantly damage features of the pictures.

Once the picture has been smoothed, sharpened and otherwise improved, the computer can embark upon the various analysis procedures. Again it is impractical to rely on box or blocks templates since boxes can be as varied as triangles. Instead 'mini-templates' are used for recognition of local elements in the picture: for instance, an array of a mere half-dozen picture points may be scrutinised and found to be part of a vertical edge. The various mini-templates can be passed over the picture in turn, matches being recorded wherever they occur.

One problem of this approach is that many different templates are needed for the various picture features – left vertical edges, bright edges, sharp edges, dim edges, fuzzy edges, etc. The task can be simplified by replacing the picture by points on a representational line drawing and then using templates to find the orientations of the lines. Sometimes the program can follow the edges of the outline drawing simply by exploring neighbouring bright points – in which case there is no need to use the templates.

When knowledge has been acquired about line orientations, short line segments can be collected together into longer lines, and similar procedures can be used to build up the full picture, stage by stage. The computer is programmed to realise that all the lines must be the boundaries of real objects. Therefore corners are signalled by lines that meet, isolated lines may not run off into space, gaps between line segments should be filled in, etc. This is analogous to how a human being uses prior knowledge to interpret visual data (eg the 'difference data' provided by stereopsis).

Pictures of blocks and other objects can also be analysed in terms of regions as well as lines. For example, it may reasonably be assumed that all picture points with the same intensity are part of the same region (in fact, imperfections in the picture generally lead to an identification of more 'meaningful' regions than are intended to exist). Programs that focus on regions aim to merge different picture areas if these are likely to be part of the same surface area. For this purpose, various rules are used by the programs (such as: 'merge adjacent areas if the difference between their average brightnesses is sufficiently small'). The region approach, like the edge approach, can produce errors: when, for example, regions are wrongly linked or wrongly kept separate. AI research aims to generate programs that can keep such errors to a minimum.

Identifying Real Objects

At the simplest level, when a computer analyses a picture it is dealing only with a two-dimensional object. The link between the picture and the three-dimensional world it represents is obvious to human beings but completely obscure to the computer. If a computer is to recognise real-world objects then it must be equipped to recognise the differences between pictures and three-dimensional scenes.

One early scene-analysis program (written by L G Roberts, 1965) was able to cope with a world inhabited by square or rectangular boxes, wedges or pyramids, or some combination of these elementary shapes. Here the program focused on basic geometric properties of the object types to predict how they would appear in a picture, and then the line drawing was investigated to verify the predictions (for example, it was assumed that two adjacent triangles must be faces of a pyramid). The program could also cope with distortions due to perspective.

Other programs (see below) have variously exploited features of the background scene (which might otherwise be confusing), and such elements as light and shadow. In the vast majority of such programs the aim is to identify objects and scenes defined by straight lines: curves bring problems of their own. It has been suggested (eg by Raphael, 1976) that vision research may have been hampered by concentrating too much on the study of outline drawings. People using vision are usually less aware of lines than of colours, textures, motion, relative positions, etc. It is also likely that future research will exploit the possibilities inherent in knowledge-based systems. We know, for instance, that visual recognition in human beings is strongly dependent upon a mass of stored information. We are enabled to perform visual acts by virtue of computational abilities and accumulated experience. Computers will become visually effective by adopting similar ploys. It may be useful, for example, for computers to organise their visual priorities much as do human beings. We tend to notice 'significant' items in a scene, not the minutiae (though we can 'home in' on an object when there is a need to do so). Our current preoccupations influence what we see; attention, influenced by cues, can vary in its focus, and this common circumstance can dramatically influence the performance of visual acts. It may be that computers will learn to focus on particular aspects of a scene, according to the prevailing task objectives.

VISION PROGRAMS

The history of artificial intelligence in any particular subject area or problem domain is largely a chronology of individual programs, separate pieces of software designed to behave intelligently in particular applications. This is true of vision research, as it is true of problem solving, game playing, theorem proving, etc. We can indicate a few vision programs as important examples in a rapidly expanding field.

Roberts, already mentioned, chose a domain comprising cubes, rectangular solids, wedges and hexagonal prisms. Then he developed a program that could analyse a photograph of a scene and identify all the visible objects. Using knowledge about the geometry of the picture-taking process (for instance, camera position and focal length), the program works back from the appearance of the picture to reality, asking whether a transformation allowed by the rules could have produced the picture using one or more of the abstract models (of cubes, prisms, etc). A mathematical assessment of the degree of fit is produced, and interpretations that fail to satisfy a threshold value are rejected.

Hence the program proceeds by making a line drawing of a photograph, then finding the model that best matches the picture. When characteristic two-dimensional features, associated with each model, are detected in a picture they are used to index the appropriate models. A *support hypothesis* assumes that each object rests on another object or on the ground. This assumption facilitates the calculation of depth.

The Roberts approach has greatly influenced later efforts in scene analysis, and other researchers have adopted different approaches. For example, Adolfo Guzman's SEE program, interpreted as a more general approach to analysing straight-line drawings, relies neither on intensive mathematical processes nor on theories used to identify the three-dimensional objects encapsulated in a two-dimensional representation. Guzman was influenced by awareness of how human beings can look at a line drawing of a jumble of solid objects and quickly identify the various components of the scene. How can a computer be made to perform the same feat?

The SEE program (developed in 1965) looks for junctions and regions in the picture, at the same time searching for clues that indicate that two regions form part of the same body. Junctions, points where two or more lines meet, are classified according to the geometry of their incident lines. The regions around the junctions are then analysed to suggest heuristics for assigning regions to one body or another. SEE was the first program to use junctions and vertices to aid the recognition of three-dimensional objects. This became a popular approach in later systems. SEE also has a daughter program, BACKGROUND, used to pick out the background in line drawings of a scene; and has been used as an integral part of an MIT robot.

G. Falk, in a similar approach to that of Roberts, developed a program (INTERPRET) that could identify the visible objects in a photograph and also determine their respective positions in three-dimensional space. However, Falk allowed for the possibility of imperfect input, in order to cope with poor views of some objects and the total absence of edges because of bad lighting. In this system, nine models were used to represent objects such as rectangular solids and wedges, and a *hypothesise-and-test* strategy was employed to identify objects in the photograph. After the objects have been recognised, a line drawing of the scene interpretation is matched with the original drawing. Use is made of heuristic procedures, as in Guzman, and later efforts (eg by Huffman and Clowes) focused on the development of a more systematic approach to scene analysis. D. Waltz expanded the work further to cope with a greater number of contingencies, and to refine the examination of adjacent junctions by means of a filtering algorithm.

These types of programs work from line drawings of scenes. By contrast, the approach of Y. Shirai is to develop systems that can *find* lines in photographs, generating lines directly from the intensity arrays. This is a difficult task because imperfections in the sensor and the photograph confuse the interpretation process: noise is interpreted by a sensitive line finder as lines, whereas a less sensitive finder misses legitimate lines.

In the Shirai approach, specific knowledge about scenes is introduced into the line-finding process. For example, if the system knows (or hypothesises) that a particular object is a block the strong lines can be used to guide a search for the weaker ones: sensitivity parameters can be adjusted to examine for suspected lines. There are ten heuristics in Shirai's program to add sophistication to the line-finding process. It is interesting that the application of particular heuristics may depend upon previous interpretations, so that the program improves with experience.

Another intelligent line-finder, written by G. R. Grape at Stanford, uses abstract models of the expected visual themes (convex polyhedra) to help it interpret incoming information. As with the Shirai program, use is made of a digitised TV image. The Grape system actively searches for lines that may be ambiguous in the local context but which are meaningful when viewed from a wider perspective. The program, like the other vision systems (and like human beings confused by shadows or 'spots before the eyes'), may make mistakes from time-to-time. For instance, an outline may be traced that is erroneous, deriving from unrelated items of data.

Such an event is, of course, an instance of artificial hallucination, a phenomenon that is not entirely inappropriate in the everyday working of sight systems. Hence Boden (1977): 'Only in a world that consistently offered perfect visual data would hallucination . . . be totally out of place . . . And predictive hallucination, or what I have called hallucination in the weak sense, is of course necessary for intelligent interpretation even of perfect data. Knowledgeable hallucination . . . is an essential part of sight.'

Another line-finding program is POPEYE, written in POP-2 at Edinburgh University (and described by Sloman, 1978). Here parts of an image are sampled until unambiguous fragments can be seen as suggesting the presence of lines. Once the process has begun, the program can build on early decisions to achieve further analysis and interpretation. For example, clusters of bar-like frag-ments can stimulate the generation of further high-level hypotheses (eg concerning alphabetic letters), a strategy that has been recognised as useful for many different types of vision sys-tems.

POPEYE needs to exploit an effective hierarchy of knowledge – beginning with knowledge of the two-dimensional dot array, mov-ing through awareness of lines and bars, to the final knowledge of (for example) letters. In addition, the program is required to know how to combine various partial elements into more meaningful wholes. Again the program, like a human being, is likely to run into error if ambiguous data is presented or if the body of information is too slight to allow useful interpretations to be made.

The various vision programs tend to belong, like most tech-nological innovation, within an evolutionary tradition. Each new vision system builds upon the features of its predecessors, and in this way refinements and new facilities are developed. Sometimes new features are incorporated at the expense of old, where a program is required to function in a specific dedicated fashion, but to a large extent new vision programs, like relatively young biolog-ical species, bear the marks of their evolutionary past. Cohen and Feigenbaum (1982) survey a wide range of vision systems. In addition to considering most of the programs mentioned above they also draw attention to (for example):

— A. K. Mackworth's POLY program used to interpret line drawings as three-dimensional scenes;

— T. Kanade's 'Origami world' and shape recovery methods;

— work on analysis of texture, motion, stereo vision, etc;

— integrated vision systems for practical applications such as robotics and aerial-photograph interpretation.

Research into artificial vision is one of the most rapidly developing AI fields today. In particular, it is being directed at automatic assembly, inspection and other computer-based facilities in the modern production environment. The central aim is that artificial vision will allow computers to interact directly with the world.

FACTORY VISION SYSTEMS

By the late-1970s automatic vision equipment was being introduced into factories in Japan, the US and elsewhere. Onda and Ohashi (1979), for example, describe the use of a television camera and solid-state image sensors to perform inspection tasks. It is emphasised that the automation of visual inspection 'is only at the first stage . . . visual inspection systems may be capable of doing only one inspection task and necessarily cannot do everything that can be done by a man'. It is part of the purpose of AI research to broaden the degree of machine competence, to enable artificial systems to behave with humanlike capabilities.

A typical visual-inspection facility includes a *process control system* to supervise the overall inspection procedure, a *sensing system* (with illumination source, imaging optics, support electronics to interface the detector, etc), an *image processing system* to extract appropriate information from the image data, and a *flaw analysis system* to interpret the data supplied by the image processor and to determine the part classification using the flaw decision rules. The image processing system, the heart of the vision facility, converts the raw sensor image data into specific image features. Features can be extracted using binary or gray-level methods, an approach which facilitates the application of automatic vision to a wide range of inspection tasks. This is a relatively new development.

In 1977, one researcher (Jarvis, cited by Myers, 1980) found only eighteen published papers covering potential applications in such areas as printed-circuit-board inspection, parts identification, light bulb filament inspection, etc. Only two cases were reported of fully automatic vision systems used in a production environment. The General Motors Sight-I system was being used to sort good chips from bad and to guide test probes to the chip contact; and a Japanese system was being employed to use local pattern techniques for the wire-bonding of transistors. The Sight-I system uses a solid-state diode array as its effective eye and a minicomputer as an image processor. The system is required to:

— determine the chip orientation;

— locate possible corners (by using a corner template);

— establish the actual corners to aid the locating of the chip;

— check the chip integrity (ie detect breaks, cracks, undersizing, fractures and missing chips).

In this type of system, the software is designed to provide the least-effective pattern-recognition facility that will allow the task to be performed. There is no need, for example, to provide sophisticated software for high resolution if the system can perform adequately without. An initial design aim, therefore, is to simplify the inspection procedure so that the minimum amount of control software is required. Even then the vision programs will have to cope with imperfections in lighting, dust, unexpected component features, etc. The more intelligent the program, the more effectively it will be able to handle unusual and unpredictable events in its environment.

It is recognised (eg in Yachida and Tsuji, 1980) that the development of Japanese vision systems has been influenced by American research into artificial intelligence. For example, AI researchers at MIT, Stanford, and SRI have tested the validity of their ideas by building hand-eye robots and various types of mobile automata. This work has helped to define the needs of practical vision systems working in the industrial environment. Such systems require, for instance, to be relatively inexpensive, to do processing in real-time, to have a low error rate, and to be flexible (ie to be able to cope with design changes in products). We have seen that vision systems comprise such elements as appropriate sensors, image processors, etc. Underlying such items are the computers that provide the necessary intelligence (the development of microprocessors has made it increasingly feasible for this to be provided on a local basis).

As with the vision programs considered above, most industrial vision systems proceed by first converting the image (produced by the sensor) into a digital form, and then processing the digital array to locate and identify product features and flaws. The detected patterns and shapes can be compared with templates to reveal the faults in the item. In one application a multiple template matching method is used to detect the position of a transistor chip entering the visual field of the microscope-assisted vidicon camera. Thereafter it is possible to test for faults in the product. Such fault-detection systems can variously exploit disparities in features that are measured, texture information, and variations in colour. Again techniques that have been developed in AI research can be exploited: for instance, edge detection methods can be used to find weld discontinuities and other imperfections in manufactured items. In such applications it is common for items to be *sorted*: defective components can be recognised and discarded (for example, into a separate bin), whereas good components can be passed on for further inspection and processing.

The need for effective economic vision facilities was underlined by the development of flexible manufacturing systems (FMS) in the 1980s, ie systems that could incorporate a variety of automated elements (robots, machine tools, conveyors, etc) and cope with a wide range of different manufacturing tasks. A 1983 report by the Tech Tran Corporation ('Machine Vision Systems: A Summary and Forecast') recognises that current flexible manufacturing systems are limited in their ability to sense the position, shape, etc of workpieces. The corollary is that vision would extend the capabilities of FMS in various ways. The report suggests that vision systems are suitable for use in inspection of parts, sorting of parts, and the guidance and control of equipment (such as robots); and that in fact there are now about 400-500 machine vision systems in use in US manufacturing plants (with new installations proceeding at a rate of about 400-500 a year).

The present technology of vision systems has a number of short-comings. For example, there is limited three-dimensional interpretation capacity and components usually have to be presented in a predetermined position. Also vision systems can be confused by poor light (leading to fuzzy images). Efforts are being made to overcome these problems. Jain and Haynes (1982), for instance, describe the relevance of fuzzy set theory to imprecision in computer vision; and Powley (1983) describes a Swedish vision system that can continue to operate successfully despite variations in lighting intensity. This robot vision system from ASEA Robotics is capable of distinguishing between 64 gradations of black/white and is unaffected by variations in levels of illumination in the normal industrial environment. In one application a system has been fitted to a robot (at ASEA Control in Vasteras, Sweden) that is required to operate a finishing station for contactor parts made in thermoset resins. The robot locates and identifies each part as it arrives on a conveyor, then selects a suitable gripper from the integral magazine, picks up the part and carries out the required deburring and flash removal sequences prior to placing the component on an out conveyor.

Sometimes a distinction is made between the two broad categories of vision-sensing equipment currently employed in manufacturing applications:

— *optical measurement systems* are computer-controlled non-contact machines used primarily to measure the dimensions of parts. They are not equipped to interpret images to make inferences about a part, but merely identify boundary points on silhouettes;

— *image recognition systems* (already considered) are designed to maximise the information about an image to aid in interpretation. They can also be reprogrammed, so re-presenting a flexible automation facility.

A constant aim, in the more sophisticated vision systems, is to simulate (or duplicate) processes carried out by human beings.

According to the Tech Tran report, the long-range objective is to create vision systems that will closely match the capabilities of the human eye and brain. Already some vision system components have performance capabilities that are analogous to those in human beings. For instance, a chip developed by Dr Savvas Chamberlain at the University of Waterloo, Canada, can detect light 5000 times better than existing devices, about as well as the human eye (reported in *Canadian Datasystems*, November 1983).

One estimate suggests that 25 per cent of robots in the US will be 'sighted' by 1990, with around 100 vision implementations in West Germany by 1989 (cited by Braggins, 1984). Today robotic guidance accounts for only 20 per cent of vision applications, with inspection and measurement applications each claiming around 40 per cent. Many companies are currently providing artificial vision facilities (see discussion in Szuprowicz, 1984; and Henkel, 1984). Most of these firms are funding research into artificial vision and rapid development can be expected in the years ahead.

Research into vision systems is being conducted in parallel in many different areas, including:

— refinements in chip technology to facilitate better light detection;

— development of the 'line striping' ('consight') system to aid component identification;

— development of fuzzy logic theory to enable vision systems to cope with partial information;

— development of algorithms to allow the various vision processes to be computed;

— development of software strategies for such tasks as edge detection, motion analysis, etc;

— development of representation formalisms specifically directed at the manipulation of vision knowledge (eg Havens and Mackworth, 1983).

Such areas of enquiry, most of them bearing directly on progress in AI, converge to facilitate the production of practical vision systems. Vision research is difficult because it is impossible for human beings to articulate the actual steps undertaken in any commonplace visual act. With problem solving and game playing, for example, the human agent can make an attempt to identify and describe the heuristics and protocols that are involved in task performance, but we do not yet know how the human brain solves problems associated with line detection and object identification. We cannot give an adequate description of 'seeing' that can thereupon be programmed for inclusion in an artificial system.

SUMMARY

This chapter has profiled various vision concerns with attention to both biological and artificial systems. We emphasise the difficulty in learning from animal vision in order to build artificial-vision systems: human beings are unable to articulate the protocols involved in visual act performance in the way that at least some of the protocols can be identified in other areas of intelligent behaviour (for example, problem solving and game playing).

Some indication is given of the range of programs designed to perform visual acts, with attention to particular software features. As with other areas of technology, an evolutionary development is discernible, later programs learning from the shortcomings of earlier. It is recognised that such AI research is directly relevant to the development of practical industrial vision systems for use in inspection, measurement and robotics.

A brief indication is given of various industrial considerations and applications in connection with working vision systems. The rapid growth of factory vision systems from the late-1970s to the 1980s is indicated (and we can expect a significant impact on employment – of, for example, inspection workers – in the future). It is recognised that there are many productivity advantages in extending automated systems so that they have sensory capabilities. The 'seeing' robot, for example, has more potential for flexible, adaptive (ie intelligent) operation than does its 'blind' brother. The productivity benefits to be expected from robots with senses is perhaps the key reason why considerable research funding will continue to be available in this field.

7 Speech, Language Understanding

INTRODUCTION

There are many ways in which speech and language relate to AI interests. There is growing emphasis on making computers more 'user-friendly', ie more able to interact with human beings without the people needing to be computer specialists (or typists). One obvious ploy is to design computers to respond to human language – in its various written, printed and spoken forms. It would obviously be convenient to be able to tell a computer what to do and then to receive its spoken comments on the practicality of the order. The provision of user-friendly interfaces that would allow this degree of two-way communication is a central aim of much current research: in particular, it is a key objective of the Japanese fifth-generation-computer programme.

Research devoted to developing the conversational abilities of computers is central to work in artificial intelligence. For example, it is a key design aim for expert systems (Chapter 8) that they be able to converse with human beings, explaining lines of reasoning, making other comments, offering advice, etc. Moreover it can also be assumed that progress in language understanding will directly affect how computers can *think* about problems in different fields. There has always been philosophic debate about the relevance of language to thought, about the importance of the various linguistic symbols to the mental powers of human beings. It is now highly significant that computer research into syntax and semantics is not only concerned with the artificial computer languages but also with the various natural languages. Psycholinguistics, programming theory and various logical formalisms are converging to develop a generalised framework for mental information processing ('cognition', 'thought') that is equally relevant to human beings and machines.

It is inevitable that, as computers become more adept at handling natural languages, they will be increasingly personalised, viewed in anthropomorphic terms. Psychologists have already begun to investigate the human tendency to regard computers as people, a tendency that will increase in the years to come. Thus Scheibe and Erwin (1980) have explored how human game-players tend to personalise computers; Neil Frude (1983) has considered the relevance of historical animism to the personalisation of computers; and Boden (1977) talks about 'programs that pass as persons'.

It is interesting that the year (1968) that saw the publication of Arthur C. Clarke's *2001: A Space Odyssey*, which features the famous conversational computer Hal, also saw the emergence of a number of programs for understanding natural language. In the 1960s, computers were already able to accept and answer questions in English in many different subject areas (for example, algebra, medicine and kinship relations), and could conduct a rudimentary psychiatric interview in English, Welsh or German. Such systems relied upon teletype facilities – and even with this limitation they invited anthropomorphisation. Today, with the rapid development of voice recognition and speech synthesis facilities, it is even more tempting to personalise computers.

Hence the various research interests that focus on matters of speech and language impinge on the question of artificial intelligence in many different ways. It is through speech and language understanding that computers will be able to develop new modes of thinking, assume more 'humanlike' attributes. Some people have been anxious that AI might lead to the creation of artificial minds, 'surrogate people', etc and that such a development may adversely affect human dignity and status. We cannot explore such value judgements in the present book, but it is worth remarking that every advance in artificial intelligence appears to give computer performance an increased resemblance to human modes of behaviour.

BIOLOGY AND LANGUAGE

As in other areas of AI work, research into speech and language understanding is likely to profit from appreciation of relevant biological phenomena. We have already seen how prior assumption, probably genetically programmed into the mammalian brain, is essential for the correct interpretation of visual information. It is likely that analogous pre-established cerebral structures are equally essential for the adequate interpretation of other complex data in nonvisual fields: for example, in the area of speech and language understanding.

We may expect a study of language to throw light on aspects of brain structure and behaviour. Thus Lashley (1950) has observed that 'Speech is the only window through which the physiologist can view cerebral life . . . the problems raised by the organisation of language seem to be characteristic of almost all other cerebral activity'. This highlights again a central feature of AI research – that there is a characteristic merging and interdependence of different cognitive phenomena and activities. We cannot usefully consider any single aspect – memory, learning, problem solving, language understanding, knowledge representation, etc – without giving attention to at least some of the others.

It is now widely believed that the human brain is structured to predispose it to accept linguistic relationships and linguistic information. Brain programs manipulate linguistic data, ordering it for storage and other purposes (and it can also be convenient to regard the brain programs as written in a language, though not in the way that speech or thought depends upon language). And we would expect the various brain programs to relate to earlier evolutionary structures. 'Biological causes run deep. One does not find complex, highly evolved life processes showing no evidence of their origin from much simpler adaptive functions. To explain language one must therefore attend to apparently unrelated aspects of intentional performance' (Trevarthen, 1974). In this sense it is convenient to regard the brain as producing language as it produces other forms of behaviour to aid the survival potential of a biological system. Language serves *intentional purposes*, working as a device to influence human behaviour – either in the originator of the language-supported thoughts or in an agent who evaluates the information being conveyed from another person. Young (1978) therefore defines language as 'any species-specific system of intentional communication between individuals'. (We can speculate on how systems developed through AI research may be deemed 'intentional'.)

In *homo sapiens*, language has immense syntactic and semantic complexity, and no other species has a comparable system for communication. It has been suggested that other primates may be able to handle several dozen distinct signs, but compared with human language this is a very primitive ability. The syntax and semantics of computer languages are less complex than those in natural languages (Russian, English, Japanese, etc) and they are evolving for computer-specific purposes, but the requirement that computers be ever more user-friendly will have implications for the future of computer languages: they will, in short, become more humanlike.

Structure is a key element in any sophisticated language system, and the notion of structure implies relationships between symbols, group hierarchies, rules for substitutions and transformations, etc. Again we can emphasise how such structural aspects are mediated by the awareness of purposes that language is supposed to serve. For example, a person sees danger and wants to warn a friend: visual perception provides the input to the linguistic system. In such a circumstance it is reasonable to infer structural and causal links between the neurons that are interested in, say, line detection and those that are involved in the structuring of sentences. The intelligence system is an integrated network, a feature that we may aim to duplicate in sophisticated AI systems.

It has been suggested that 'many properties of grammar are present in some form in prelinguistic perceptuo-motor behaviour' (Osgood, 1971). This neatly illustrates how language in man evolved from earlier nonlinguistic modes of behaviour, and today represents a range of encoding and decoding abilities that developed from related skills that had evolved for other purposes. Many of the linguistic computational abilities are concerned with manipulating the relationships that define the linguistic structure, and such abilities – because of the evolutionary background – are at least partly preprogrammed into the human brain. Human infants, before they can speak or understand, have special detectors that are uniquely sensitive to speech sounds (and the early 'burblings' and 'gurglings', seemingly meaningless, are already influenced in their character by the prevailing language of the infant's environment).

A study of how language is learned can help to uncover its complexities. We may, for example, trace the development of linguistic usage in the child, moving from early babbling, through the acquisition of simple 'label words' (*mama, dada,* etc), to the use of first-order relationship symbols that begin the acquisition of a structural linguistic ability. The gradual development of comprehension can be examined in the same way – from both the passive end (where the child gives behavioural evidence of understanding given linguistic statements) and the active end (where the child generates a statement to signal intended action or to influence the behaviour of other people in the environment).

The decoding of speech depends upon the person (or machine) being able to make reference to a body of stored knowledge. A word is interpreted within a spectrum of expectations influenced by the context of the linguistic experience. If a friend is talking we are unconsciously (sometimes consciously) anticipating both the words that will be used and their intended meaning. This suggests constant reference to a knowledge base, a circumstance that has implications for the design of artificial systems that are capable of understanding language. Speech cannot be decoded without a store 'of *a priori* knowledge about the language . . . Every speaker or listener carries in his cortex a vast store of information about any languages he uses' (Fry, 1970). It is one of the tasks of the neurophysiologists to find out how this linguistic knowledge is encapsulated in brain structures.

The more complex the stored knowledge, the most difficult it is to access it quickly for pattern-recognition or thinking processes. A sequential search of *all* the knowledge would obviously be highly inefficient, and various search strategies are employed to allow a person to 'home in' on the specific areas of knowledge that are relevant to the task in hand. In human beings there are also a variety of psychological constraints that influence how effectively a piece of language is understood. For example, the speed of understanding must keep pace with the rate of speech; and sentences must be understood as the words are delivered chronologically (sometimes several words must be given before the analysis can get started). People, like computers, vary in their language-understanding competence: this may or may not indicate the existence of both common and disparate linguistic mechanisms from one person to another.

The mechanisms for understanding printed and spoken words are closely related to the mechanisms for perception and pattern recognition. As with other forms of perceptual processing, language is analysed by a combination of two sorts of mechanisms:

— with *data-driven, bottom-up* mechanisms, the relevant processes are stimulated by signals arriving at the system (in the case of language processing in human beings, at the eyes and ears). 'Bottom-up' signifies that the analysis begins with the lowest level of information – sensory data;

— with *conceptually-driven, top-down* mechanisms, the analysis begins with the expectations and cues that are always available. Conceptually-guided processing helps to frame expectations about the subject matter, about the information that is likely to arrive ('I knew what she was going to say next'). Here analysis is from high-level structures to low-level data.

It is generally assumed that both data-driven and conceptually-driven approaches work together in human language understanding and other perceptual acts. Again there are clues as to what we may expect in an AI system designed to cope with language. One requirement is likely to be software routines variously equipped to handle individual words, grammatical classes (noun, preposition, etc), and specific sentence components (noun phrase, verb phrase, etc). Other routines can be devoted to integrating the findings of routines, using the knowledge base for comparison purposes, and other semantic matters. The top-down sentence and meaning routines allow the overall system to work quickly and in a way that is relatively insensitive to errors in the sensory analysis. But the system may come to expect things that will never happen, and so must be amenable to correction by data-driven routines. In human language-understanding systems, and ideally in the analogous AI systems, there is scope for abandoning one procedure, if seen to be fruitless, and trying another.

Cognitive psychology describes the language-understanding task in information-processing terms that can be interpreted in a computer context. Thus there is talk of how language enables human beings to encode the structural networks in their memory systems and to express them using (written or spoken) symbols. The human being, trying (usually) to be 'person-friendly', adapts the symbolic expressions deemed most likely to be accessible to the other person. The intelligent computer, aiming to be user-friendly, will evolve a similar adaptive potential.

Miller and Johnson-Laird (1976) suggested that understanding a sentence is analogous to running a program on a computer. Just as a program is *compiled*, and then *run* (with respect to the relevant data), so the person *translates* the natural-language input into a set of mental instructions and then *decides* how to respond. In essence, this approach may be regarded as offering a procedural semantics. The important consideration is that this approach offers an information-processing analysis of language understanding that does not depend upon any specific type of hardware. The corollary is that language can in principle be understood as an array of neurons, an array of silicon chips, or an array of anything else – provided that the necessary procedures and protocols are embedded in the configuration.

The study of the relationships between computer languages and the computers on which they are used indicates how brain structures may be revealed by a study of natural language. Thus Sampson (1975) asks: 'what is to human language as the internal mechanisms of a computer are to the computer's language ... what kind of a computer would use languages of the kind we have identified as natural languages?' This again illustrates the reciprocal influence of cognitive psychology and computer science: a study of language understanding in *homo sapiens* helps us to frame analogous procedures for computers, and a study of computer languages gives clues about possible brain structures.

The biology (and psychology) of language understanding in

people will continue to influence attempts to define artefacts with similar powers, and psychological theories will be mediated by what we know of computer performance. Sampson suggests it is possible to develop a theory of the human mind based on Chomsky's theory of language, using the strategy of comparing 'Man with another type of organism which uses complex languages, namely the digital computer'. The approach to language understanding in artificial systems, described below, has been influenced by what we know of language understanding in *homo sapiens*.

LANGUAGE UNDERSTANDING

General

Soon after computers first became available in the 1940s it was obvious that they would find application in many linguistic areas. The evident ability of the computer to handle symbols allowed it to compile indexes from text and to generate concordances (indexes than included a line of context for each entry). These tasks were computationally simple, requiring the computer to do nothing more than count and arrange data in particular ways. It was soon felt that computers might perform more ambitious linguistic tasks.

Machine translation (see below) was one of the first application areas that extended the linguistic activity of computers. One of the early researchers, Warren Weaver, suggested in 1949 that computers might be useful for 'the solution of world-wide translation problems'. Initially the task of machine translation seemed relatively straightforward – which led to an optimism later found to be unfounded. The idea was that the computer would look up the words in a bilingual dictionary and process the findings to produce suitable sentences in the output language. In fact many problems afflict these seemingly simple tasks.

It was soon recognised that computers might do better at translation if they had a degree of understanding of the texts they were handling. Such a facility would enable them, it was thought, to cope with the peculiarities of individual languages. The approach to helping machines to understand the textual material they were handling is a central feature of work in artificial intelligence (we saw in Chapter 1 that *understanding* was involved in any comprehensive definition of intelligence). Some of the AI work in this field involves the use of knowledge-based systems to model human language and the development of computer programs that would serve as functional implementations of such models. Barr and Feigenbaum (1981) have identified four historical categories of natural language programs:

— some programs (eg BASEBALL, SAD-SAM, STUDENT and ELIZA) aimed to generate limited results in narrow domains. By keeping the processes simple, many of the problems of natural language could be ignored;

— in some early systems (such as PROTO-SYNTHEX I), a representation of the text was stored, indexing devices being employed to aid retrieval of particular words or phrases. Since the stored text could cover any subject the systems were not restricted, by virtue of their structure, to a particular domain. However, such systems were weak on semantics and had no deductive powers;

— limited-logic systems (eg SIR, TLC, DEACON and CON-VERSE) aimed to translate input sentences into the formal notation used in the database. Here the aim was to allow deductions to be made from information held in the data-base, even though only a few of the processes used in everyday conversation could be exploited;

— knowledge-based systems (eg LUNAR and SHRDLU) most closely linked to current work in artificial intelligence, use information about the particular subject domain to understand the input sentences. Such programs, some of which are expert systems (Chapter 8), have various deductive and other powers.

The main difficulty in developing programs to understand natural language is the sheer complexity of everyday communication. It has long been possible to formalise aspects of everyday discourse but such efforts have only related to a small proportion of the processes that occur in natural-language usage. It is still true that we do not understand the complexities of natural language, and so we cannot write compilers for English or Japanese. At the same time, various strategies are being developed to enable computers to handle natural-language discourse. Most of these strategies rely upon modelling how human beings cope with linguistic communication. For example, people need to store information about the meanings of words (how words relate to each other, how words relate to particular behavioural manifestations), about how to transcribe one linguistic expression into another logically-equivalent one, and about how new (more up-to-date) linguistic information can be used to modify or replace existing stored information.

By the 1980s much attention had already been given to how knowledge could be stored to aid linguistic understanding in computer systems (see, for example, Tennant, 1978). Subsequent work has focused on developing this knowledge-based approach with the aim of making it easier for human beings to interrogate intelligent machines. Already modern database management systems often include query languages to augment programming language access, but in general such languages can only be used by specialists. The user of a typical query language must have a good idea of what is in the database, must know how the knowledge is formalised and encoded, and must be able to cope with the specialised syntax and semantics of the query languages. Clearly this degree of expertise will not be found in the typical everyday user wanting to converse with a computer. There are obvious advantages in giving computers their own understanding of natural language. There are already commercial natural-language systems available, but many of the problems associated with linguistics have not yet been solved.

It is still true that users are mostly expected to communicate with computers using highly structured, computer-imposed techniques. A few familiar English (or French or German, etc) words are allowed but only within specific (unnatural) formats. At the same time, progress in natural-language processing is influencing the character of commercial products. For example, the Intellect system, developed by the Artificial Intelligence Corporation (AIC) and now marketed by IBM, is able to translate typed English requests into formal database query languages and to present the requested information to the enquirer. Intellect can respond effectively even if semantically equivalent requests are written in different ways. It has been suggested that a natural-language system should be able to answer users' requests well over ninety per cent of the time (Harris of AIC claims that Intellect easily meets that requirement – 'No one cares why it doesn't work. When people sit down to use the system, it's got to deliver').

Most natural-language processing systems run on large-scale computers. Intellect, for example, runs on IBM 4300 systems and larger mainframes, with one version for Prime Computer super-minicomputers (it requires up to 1M byte of memory for the load module). At the same time it is suggested that Intellect will not need to lose much of its power to run on microcomputers operating with less-complex data (though it will require a fair bit of 'technological shoehorning' – Harris). There are in fact a number of natural-language systems available for microcomputers, with others planned.

The Symantec spin-off from the Machine Intelligence Corporation aims to develop language-processing systems for micros, with the IBM Personal Computer in mind. The company is now incorporating AI features in software that will have a natural-language processing capacity. It is recognised that successes on large machines have led to the feasibility of scaled down versions of AI programs for smaller machines. Another company, Cognitive Systems, is developing systems that will have extensive domain knowledge and knowledge also of natural language. Here the products will include natural-language 'front-ends' for database query systems and also expert systems that can advise users on specific topics. And in 1984 the American Frey Associates software house (in Amherst, N.H.) began delivery of a natural language database query language that makes use of AI techniques to enlarge its vocabulary without any help from a programmer.

The Themis package from Frey, intended initially to run on Digital Equipment Corporation's VAX family of superminicomputers, can be easily expanded by a human operator ('We'll deliver Themis with a basic vocabulary of over 900 words, and the ease with which users can add new ones means it can then be tailored for a variety of special applications' – Eric D Frey). Themis is written in InterLisp and requires up to 2M bytes of main memory. It can translate conversational-English queries into a 'language-understander module', the language understander again being used to translate the retrieved database information for display on the terminal screen. (Themis responds 'politely but firmly' to expletives.)

We can expect the range of commercial natural-language products to increase in the years ahead. Japan has marked out natural-language systems as a theme for the next phase (1985-1989) of the ten-year fifth-generation project; and Western companies are increasingly active in this field. Already many US companies (eg Bolt, Beranek and Newman of Cambridge, MA and SRI of Palo Alto, CA) have many years development experience in natural-language systems, work which has yielded such systems as RUS and Dialogic. In Europe there are various University projects (eg the Hamans system at the University of Hamburg and the database-access facility at the University of Cambridge). More initiatives may be expected from the centrally funded ESPRIT and Alvey programmes.

Syntax, Semantics and Logic

The study of both machine and natural language has traditionally focused on *syntax* and *semantics*. The syntax of a language defines how the strings of symbols that comprise the sentences of the language are formally structured, without at this stage considering what the sentences mean. *Grammar* is often regarded as a synonym for syntax. It is important, when studying syntax, to ascertain which strings of symbols are grammatical within the language. *Semantics* is concerned with what the symbols and sentences actually mean.

Linguistic analysis usually involves exploring first the syntax of an expression and then the semantics, a chronology that was adopted in the early work on automation translation from one language to another. But it was quickly seen that, in natural language, syntax and semantics often merged in inconvenient ways and that it became impossible to study the semantics of a natural language without considering also the structure of the language in question. This discovery was to have various implications for the study of computer languages and the use of AI techniques for linguistic purposes.

Particular research programmes also influenced the approach to AI work in computational linguistics. For example, Chomsky's theory of generative grammar radically affected work in linguistics, including attitudes to how computers could be given an understanding of linguistic expressions. One approach is for language-processing programs to use grammatical rules to *parse* the input sentences, ie to analyse the symbolic expressions and to provide thereby clues as to what the various parts of a sentence might mean. Parsing components are virtually universal in natural-language-processing systems, but it has so far proved impossible to explore all types of natural-language expressions using parsing processes.

Today increasing attention is being directed at exploring the underlying logic (or logics) of language. Chomsky's linguistic analysis, for example, is virtually an enquiry in symbolic logic and the various ways of exploring language-related knowledge representations depend upon symbolic formalisms of various sorts. The syntax (grammar) of a natural language is a patterned structure that can also be formalised in symbolic terms. It is the possibility of formalising aspects of natural language that allows linguistic understanding to be modelled in artificial systems.

Research highlighted by Webber (1983) and others shows how logic and deduction are relevant to the generation of natural language. For example, producing a successful sentence may require reasoning about the competence of other people: we take into account what a person is likely to know before we make a remark. Ideally a computer would do the same when addressing a human user. Moreover the limitations of first-order logic, concerned as it is with eternal truths, suggest that other formalisms need to be developed to cope with a changing world. Modal logic is interested in relating knowledge to action as a means of exploring the characteristics of 'possible worlds'. This approach is also relevant to the task of language generation.

We have suggested that everyday language relies on a range of reasoning techniques that can handle simple first-order relations, the properties of a changing world, common sense, fuzzy information, etc. The complexity of these disparate techniques is one of the central reasons why it is difficult to build a sophisticated conversational ability and language understanding into computer programs.

Some Programs

A number of natural-language programs – ranging from BASEBALL and ELIZA at one extreme to LUNAR and SHRDLU at the other – have already been mentioned. Today there are many linguistic programs available for a wide range of different purposes, and the development of such programs has been conducted in parallel with the various efforts of linguistic specialists to understand the character of natural language, its syntax and semantics. Many of the programs have been written to demonstrate a particular language-processing capability; a few attempt to display a generalised conversational ability.

The BASEBALL system, developed at MIT in 1960, used a data file containing the month, day, place, teams and score of every baseball game played in the American League in one season. The program could answer almost any query relating to the store of data (eg 'To whom did the Red Sox lose on June 19th?', 'What was the score at the New York game on September 26th?').

The STUDENT system, developed at MIT in 1964, was concerned with the solution of algebra problems as they are stated in textbooks or puzzle books. Here the system could only cope with a relatively narrow range of English expressions. The STUDENT knowledge base contained some general information about geometric, algebraic and arithmetic matters (eg that distance equals velocity times time).

The ELIZA program, perhaps the most cited of all the language programs, was developed by Joseph Weizenbaum in 1966. The program is written to assume the role of a psychiatrist in conversation with a human patient. In fact, as Weizenbaum would be the first to admit, ELIZA works by semantic trickery. There is no understanding of linguistic matters or of the subject domain in which the 'conversation' takes place. (Weizenbaum and others have been concerned at the readiness with which some people have been prepared to anthropomorphise the inanimate ELIZA system.)

The ARPA SUR (speech understanding research) project yielded a range of linguistic programs designed to demonstrate various automatic language-understanding abilities. Under the terms of the overall programme five different speech projects were initiated and various subcontracts placed for developing components for speech systems. Bolt, Beranek and Newman produced SPEECHLIS and HWIM (Hear What I Mean). By 1976 Carnegie-Mellon University had produced a number of different programs: HEARSAY-I, DRAGON, HARPY and HEARSAY-II. And SRI International also developed a speech understanding program in collaboration with SDC. (These programs are described in detail in Barr and Feigenbaum, 1981.)

The LUNAR program, rated by many observers as one of the most successful language-processing systems, was developed to help human users to analyse the rocks brought back from the moon. The system first works out the meaning of the user's query, and then answers the question. This language-processing facility is essentially a type of expert system: it assesses enquiries against a detailed knowledge-base, in this case in the field of geology, and then provides a specific detailed response.

The SHRDLU program, again much publicised, represents a robot that shows its understanding by replying to a human user and by behaving in certain ways at the human's command. Here the simulated robot contains an internal representation of its own acts and a model of the external world. This enables the 'robot' to cope with questions that would otherwise be unmanageable. SHRDLU, like other AI programs (see Chapter 6), is interested in the 'blocks world'. It can carry on a conversation with a human user, the program answering questions, pointing out when a query is ambiguous or obscure, declaiming 'OK' when it carries out a command, and quite likely to say 'You're welcome!' when finally thanked by the human user.

With the growing importance being attached to 'user-friendliness', emphasis will continue to be given to the importance of language-understanding systems. The development of expert systems will also place a premium on the ability of computers to respond to enquiries couched in written or spoken natural language. The translation from natural language to machine-understandable language has to occur, at some stage, wherever there is an interface between people and intelligent machines. The aim with many linguistic programs is to enable the computer, rather than the human being, to perform the translation. This highlights a central feature in AI research – that there is a constant hunt for means of automating intelligent tasks, ie of programming the cognitive capacities that characterise human beings.

VOICE SYSTEMS

General

Voice systems in human beings can function in either input or output modes, ie we can speak and hear. One purpose of AI development is to enable computers to synthesise voices (male, female, young, old, in any known language) and to recognise the voices of people (or computers) replying to them. Voice-recognition and speech-synthesis systems will increasingly feature in commercial products, and such facilities will be commonplace in the interface provisions of new-generation computers. A number of observers (eg Kirvan, 1984) have suggested that the speech technology industry is now ready for major expansion.

Voice input can conveniently be divided into speech recognition and speaker verification (it is one thing to recognise a voice, quite another to understand what a person is saying). Similarly, voice output can be seen as comprising speech coding and speech synthesis. In one type of specialised product (called a voice store-and-forward system), spoken words are stored for future retrieval by other users. These and other facilities will progressively improve the man/machine interface in the years to come. It will be possible to speak to computers, in any language, and for them to answer back. Already there are a number of experimental devices that use a combination of speech input and speech output to aid communication with human users. For example, an electropneumatic robotic device (Henthorn and Dawson, 1983), formerly speech-controlled, now also carries a vocal response unit. The aim of such work is to explore the feasibility of using speech input and output to control a robotic system.

It is also anticipated that speech recognition and generation technology will enhance existing telecommunications facilities. Text messaging has already been very successful where people have access to terminals and the associated computers, but voice messaging could be even more effective since there would be no requirement for standard terminals. Many organisations are now exploring the possibilities for development in these areas. The Bell-Northern research/INRS-Telecom team, for instance, is now researching the efficient coding of speech for digital transmission and also looking at the design of man/machine communication systems. The communication research includes the development of techniques for the computer recognition of spoken information, the computer production of speech, and the design of communication protocols that integrate these techniques for practical applications.

As we would expect, there are different research problems in speech input and speech output. It is relatively easy, for example, to define the requirements of speech synthesis, though voice intonation can bring problems. Without a detailed knowledge of semantics – beyond the grasp of current machines – computers cannot decide, in any convincing way, when to emphasise a word or when to raise or lower their voice. In speech input (ie when the computer is required to recognise what is being said) a main problem is that the human voice, variously affected by emotion, alcohol, fatigue, etc, is an extremely inconsistent transmitter. Factors such as volume, accent and ambient noise can also make it extremely difficult for a computer to derive any sense from what human beings are saying in its environment. Artificially synthesised sentences can now be produced in a variety of contexts, but it is extremely unusual for a computer-based system to be able to recognise connected speech with much consistency.

Voice Recognition, Speech Understanding

People have speculated, for at least two thousand years, on the possibility of artefacts being able to recognise and understand human speech. Only in recent years, however, has this become a feasible research endeavour. The possibility of the machine recognition of spoken words has been explored for a few decades though, at least by the mid-1970s, the results had been 'frustratingly poor' (Raphael, 1976).

In human beings, the ear detects sound waves which are then converted into nerve pulses for transmission to the brain. Similarly, a microphone converts sound waves into electrical pulses for subsequent interpretation. It is this interpretation task that is at the heart of the speech-recognition problem. An early step towards solving it was taken by an acoustics engineer about thirty years ago. He built a box of electronic equipment with a red light on top and linked to a microphone. Whenever anyone in the vicinity mentioned the word 'watermelon' the light would flash! Unfortunately this engagingly successful device did not point the way to effective speech-recognition systems. There are around 10,000 words commonly used in conversation, and 'watermelon', apparently, is unusually easy to recognise. The ensuing spate of bigger and better watermelon boxes only led to about 100 words ever being recognised, and only if these were pronounced very carefully, one at a time, and by a speaker to whom the system had been tuned. A different approach was needed.

One approach relied on integrating various acoustic techniques with the most successful linguistic and question-answering techniques. The aim was to develop a speech understanding system that contains a range of acoustic, syntactic and semantic elements tailored to a particular subject domain. One such subject domain is the game of chess, used in a speech-understanding system developed at Carnegie-Mellon University in 1971. Here it was found that the system could not easily distinguish between the words 'queen' and 'king' – an evident limitation! By the mid-1970s a few experimental speech-understanding systems were being developed, and it became clear that systems already able to handle, albeit slowly, more than a hundred words would be capable of enhancement to provide much more competent systems.

It was obvious that voice-recognition and speech-understanding systems would need to model at least some of the processes occurring in the analogous human systems. The computer uses an analogue-to-digital converter to digitise the voice information received (this is equivalent to how the ear converts sound waves into electrical pulses). When the data stored is a mathematical translation of a three-dimensional waveform, the information can serve as an effective template. Template-matching is the most common approach to voice recognition.

Most voice-recognition systems are speaker-dependent (ie they can only cope with words spoken by the same person), so the person must first speak each word of the required vocabulary to allow the system to generate reference templates. The larger the vocabulary, the larger the memory required by the computer. Once the reference templates are in place, the speaker can utter a word: the computer system 'hears' it, via a microphone, converts it into pulses, and makes reference to the stored template for that word, whereupon a match is found and the computer responds accordingly. The technique of *Linear Predictive Coding* (LPC) has been developed as a system of mathematical analysis that enables the computer to use fewer numbers when storing template details, so facilitating significant memory savings. It is also possible to use *features analysis* to enable a sound's phonetic characteristics, instead of waveform data, to be stored.

There are many speech elements that can be used to aid the tasks of voice recognition and speech understanding. We have already mentioned such elements as phonetics, syntax and semantics. There are also *phonemics* (where pronunciations vary when words are spoken together in sentences), *morphemics* (combining *morphemes*, units of meaning, to form words, as with plurals, conjugations, etc), *prosodics* (where stress and intonation vary), and *pragmatics* (where conversation may be influenced by the speaker's intentions). Underlying the scrutiny of such speech elements is the holding of relevant information, not only template data but also the domain-specific knowledge without which a computer could not aspire to semantic understanding.

The various theoretical and research programmes have yielded a growing range of practical products. For instance, the Nippon Electricity Company launched the Voice Data Input Terminal in 1978, a device able to recognise up to 120 words, spoken continuously in groups of up to five words. This followed the voice recognition units introduced in 1976 by the US firm Threshold Technology Inc. IBM researchers at Yorktown Heights used a computer in 1980 to transcribe spoken sentences from a 1000-word vocabulary read at normal speaking pace (91 per cent accuracy was claimed). At the same time the Scott Instruments Corporation was introducing the Vet-1 voice-entry terminal, to be followed by a Vet-2 model with enhanced performance.

Many other companies (Interstate Electronics, Auricle, Voicetek, Texas Instruments, Centrigram, etc) have now launched voice recognition units, and many more systems are under development. Iverson et al (1982) consider some of the software features of such systems. Voice recognition facilities have now been introduced into the industrial control room, high-speed aircraft, factories and offices. Steps towards speaker-independent voice-recognition systems (Schalk and van Meir, 1983) and towards greatly enlarged vocabularies have brought forward the day when voice input and output will be commonplace elements in computer interfaces. The Medical Communication Corp., for instance, has developed a microcomputer-based device, the Voice Processor, which can recognise up to 25,000 words. The design relied on reducing the amount of memory needed to recognise a word, allowing a vastly increased vocabulary to be held in the same memory space. Many applications are envisaged for this type of product.

Voice Input, the UK agent of the US Votan company, has introduced a speaker-independent speech-recognition system. Though the device is extremely limited in scope it is pointing the way towards computer systems that will understand what anybody says to them. IBM and Hewlett-Packard are now offering a commercial range of standard speech input facilities, and such provisions will become widespread in the years to come. Already about half-a-dozen large telecommunications companies have demonstrated devices that act under spoken instructions from human beings. A device from NEC recognises connected speech and can also translate between Japanese, English and Spanish! But Yasuo Kato, the general manager of NEC's Yawasaki computer and communications research centre has declared that 'we're 10 or 20 years off a speaker-independent, large vocabulary, connected-speech-recognition system'.

AI research into voice-recognition and speech-understanding systems has already yielded a plethora of functional products. This is highly significant in view of the fact that linguistic philosophy is still a hotly debated topic. There is no consensus on how language usage and understanding in human beings are to be interpreted, yet artificial systems are rapidly developing their speech and language faculties.

Speech Synthesis

Speech-synthesis facilities can be linked to voice-recognition units or they can function on their own (companies with an interest in machine speech capabilities tend to be interested in both input and output). A speech-synthesis system may be used to 'shout' a warning in dangerous factory circumstances, or to signal hazards in other types of environment: for instance, the McDonnell-Douglas Corporation have produced an Aural Cockpit Warning System using micro-controlled speech synthesis. Or speech-synthesis facilities can be used in offices, cars and the domestic environment (some toys and games use speech-synthesis techniques).

There are various ways in which speech can be synthesised but these usually fall into one of two main categories. In *copy synthesis* the output is simply a copy of prerecorded speech, whereas in *synthesis-by-rule* the speech is constructed from analysis of the input under the control of rules specified in a computer program. The use of rules allows economies to be made in the amount of storage that is needed, but also demands an understanding of the structure of speech. Synthesis by rule can be used to generate intelligible speech from unrestricted text, by employing letter-to-sound rules and a suitable mathematical representation of the human voice. Most effective speech-synthesis systems of this sort have been limited to large computers, but now there are signs that micro-based speech-synthesis by rule may soon be possible.

Speech-synthesis chips have already been designed for many different products. As early as 1978 a speech-synthesiser chip, the TMC 0280 appeared in the Speak and Spell learning aid from Texas Instruments. This was one of the first speech-synthesis chips to exploit Linear Predictive Coding (LPC) methods, already mentioned in connection with voice recognition. Here a 131,072-bit ROM can carry 165 words, its output supplying the various pitch, amplitude and filter parameters from which the chip can build the necessary speech waveforms.

By 1980 many products could synthesise their own speech in response to various types of input (including queries). Votrax developed portable speech synthesisers for the vocally impaired, and also launched a Business Communicator able to translate up to

64 telephone Touch-Tone inputs into an audio output. Other products emerged from such companies as Intelligent Systems, IBM, etc.

Speech synthesis is, strictly speaking, not a problem in artificial intelligence. It involves a host of technological difficulties and various strategies have been adopted to make it effective (see, for example, the discussion of waveform synthesis, constructive synthesis and analysis synthesis in Brightman and Crook, 1982). But speech synthesis in isolation lacks the connection with cognitive processes that makes speech *understanding* such a central AI field. There is a clear sense in which speech synthesis is the other side of the aural communication coin, but as a separate technology it requires no insights into semantics or machine thought.

TRANSLATION

In the early days of computing it was believed that certain syntactic transformations could be applied to natural language without distorting the meaning. One of the results of this belief was a great effort in the 1950s to have computers translate text from one language to another. Multilingual dictionaries were set up on computer tape, and grammars were developed to indicate the differences (in word order, noun cases, etc) in the various natural languages. This work, however, was largely unsuccessful, the generated translations being usually unreliable and inaccurate. (One example often quoted is the translation of 'The spirit is willing but the flesh is weak' into Russian and then back into English to give 'The wine is agreeable but the meat has spoiled'.) A central lesson learned from the early failures was that the line between syntax and semantics is extremely hazy, a difficulty that is less evident in the artificial languages developed for the writing of computer programs.

Today there are well over a dozen translation systems (WEIDNER, LAGOS, ALPS, etc) that serve as aids for the professional translator. Few automatic systems would be trusted to provide unaided translations with an acceptable degree of accuracy. Some systems produce a raw translation which is then edited by a human being; and some are interactive, able to ask the human translator for help when they encounter problems. But the task facing both human and machine translators should not be underestimated: there are around 5000 languages and dialects spoken in the world, and with increased communication across national boundaries there will be a growing requirement for translation services.

Some observers view the prospect of automatic translation with great optimism. Thus Rouvray and Wilkinson (1984) declare: 'we are convinced that, for particular applications, all major languages will be translated by computer by the early 1990s'. The possibilities for machine translation developed rapidly in the 1960s following the work of Zellig Harris and Noam Chomsky. It became possible to devise logical rules for the analysis of language, a development that aided the computerisation of linguistic acts. Today millions of words a year are translated, with the help of computers, by such organisations as ITT, Xerox, General Motors and the Commission of the European Communities in Luxembourg. The most successful translations are in the fields of science, technology, law and administration: computers cannot yet master the subtleties of creative writing.

One of the most successful translation packages is SYSTRAN, first installed nearly a decade ago and today running on an IBM 370/158 computer. Already this type of system is handling around 20 per cent of the French-to-English translation and about 50 per cent of the English-to-Italian for the European Commission. Rouvray and Wilkinson (1984) highlight some of the most effective translation systems, including SYSTRAN, WEIDNER, ALPS, SPANAM, TAUB, CULT, SMART and SUSY. Efforts are made to reassure human translators that computers are unlikely to replace large numbers of employees, but some observers (eg Durham, 1983) acknowledge that machine translation with *no* human involvement is the long-term research goal. Already the European Eurotra project is aiming to dramatically reduce the amount of initial translation and post-editing required by human beings. (The research may also overcome SYSTRAN's habit of translating 'hydraulic ram' into the equivalent of 'water goat'.)

Machine translation was originally viewed as a simple matter of replacing words in one language by words in another. It was only later that the many syntactic and semantic problems became evident. Progress in artificial intelligence, helping machines to understand language, will increase the effectiveness of computer translation, particularly in the areas where subtleties and ambiguities characterise the texts in question.

SUMMARY

This chapter has drawn attention to some of the AI concerns that relate to speech and language understanding. We can see that information can be conveyed in written (or printed) and spoken forms, and that computers are developing both speech input and speech output capabilities. Again the relevance of certain biological and psychological considerations is emphasised: much of the work on speech and language understanding is an effort to model the analogous processes to be found in human beings.

Efforts to develop such abilities in computers bear on various product-development plans. One requirement is that computers develop an effective conversational ability, so that – as in expert systems – they can advise human beings working in a particular subject domain. Another requirement is that man/machine interfaces be rendered more user-friendly for a wide range of applications – providing enhanced computer assistance to the disabled, facilitating the educational use of computers, allowing complex control systems to communicate more effectively with their human users, etc.

For such tasks there is often a requirement that computers be able to recognise the human voice, *any* human voice, and to respond by generating the appropriate speech. Speaker-independent voice recognition is one of the main AI research goals; computers can already synthesise speech in many languages and in various phonetic modes (male, female, young, old, and to convey various physiological or psychological states, eg anger, intoxication, fear, etc).

Many of the language-handling tasks needed in modern society are influenced by progress in artificial-intelligence research. We have mentioned machine translation from one language to another, but there are many other language-handling tasks not covered in the present chapter. For example, there are now programs available to write summaries ('abstracts') of articles or new items, to write fables and short stories, to produce poetry (eg Japanese haiku), and to generate text for other research, artistic and practical purposes. The handling of language has proved to be one of the most important influences on the development of modern society. Intelligent machines with language-handling capacities will be crucial aids for human beings in the years to come.

Part 3

USES, PRODUCTS AND TRENDS

8 Expert Systems*

INTRODUCTION

Expert systems are often regarded as representing a subclass of artificial intelligence, and they are often (wrongly) identified with fifth-generation computers. Expert systems have been working – with varying degrees of success – for many years, whereas we do not expect to see true fifth-generation configurations until around the end of the decade. However, as conversational systems relying on progress in knowledge engineering (Chapter 5), expert systems are one of the key developments contributing to the international fifth-generation programme.

In one view (eg Addis, 1982), the range of expert systems represents degrees of enhancement to an information retrieval system. This type of interpretation is obviously plausible: the competence of the human expert largely resides in fancy information retrieval skills, and whatever the ideal purpose of the artificial system it is easy to extend the analogy, in this context, between machine and human capability. It has been pointed out that much of human problem-solving is possible through the exploitation of 'non-standard' logics, allowing a flexibility that is not yet possible in artificial systems, but it is for this reason that the various facets of inference-making are being explored as part of expert-system research.

An expert system may be regarded as a means of recording and accessing human competence in a particular specialist field. The

* This chapter is based partly on Chapter 4 from *Towards Fifth-Generation Computers* (NCC Publications, 1983).

most robust interpretation (eg Duda et al, 1980) suggests that an expert system is capable of humanlike performance and can serve thereby as a replacement expert. Less ambitiously, expert systems may be seen as exhibiting competence in a relatively narrow agreed domain, serving as tools to aid communication between human experts. (It is hard to see this latter interpretation not progressively yielding to the former with advances in knowledge engineering and other areas.) The fact that no expert system has so far been built for completely naive human users underlines one particular thrust behind the fifth-generation research programme: here a central aim is to make computer capability, embodied in expert and other types of systems, available to the widest possible range of users. If current expert systems are reasonably seen to lack natural human performance features then future systems will be less limited – and, ideally, they will be found in schools, offices, shops and the home, as well as in the specialist research environments which have tended to be the domain of working expert systems.

We have seen that work in information retrieval (IR) is likely to influence the development of expert systems. A main purpose of IR is to extract relevant information from a large store of data. The elements in the store are usually assigned index terms which the user specifies, in some combination, to obtain the required information. One key problem is that the index terms, in different concatenations, are capable of many different interpretations: when words are combined in phrases, there can be many subtle variations that are difficult to express in Boolean or other types of formal logic. This circumstance may make it difficult for the user to obtain the specific information that he requires. This type of problem is common to the development of both IR facilities and expert systems.

One approach to information retrieval is to develop a model of the stored data so that it is homomorphic with respect to user requests. Such a model would feature the index terms in defined relationships in order to aid information selection in the particular subject area. Again, work in this area has direct relevance to requirements in both mainstream IR and expert systems: Addis (1982), for example, has noted what he sees to be 'an evolutional convergence of what may seem to be two distinct sciences'.

Some of the most successful expert systems are now relatively well known and have been operating for several years. Typical of such systems are MYCIN and INTERNIST (for medical diagnosis), DENDRAL and SECS (for chemical analysis), and PROSPECTOR (for geological prospecting) (see Actual Expert Systems, below). GPS (the General Problem Solver) has also been regarded as one of the earliest expert systems. DENDRAL and SECS are said to have 'as much reasoning power in chemistry as most graduate students and some Ph.Ds in the subject' (Cole, 1981).

The expert system SIR and its successor QA3 are question-answering systems exploiting the techniques of formal logic. The LUNAR program, already discussed, can answer questions about moon rock samples by drawing on a massive database provided by NASA: here procedural semantics allows questions to be automatically converted into a program to be executed by a sophisticated retrieval facility.

An initial step in generating an expert system may be to persuade a human expert to sit at a computer terminal and to type in his or her expertise. We have seen that this can be an immensely difficult task: it is one thing to be an expert, quite another to be able to articulate the expertise in coherent propositions that are useful to a computer. Developments in knowledge engineering may be expected to aid the expert in this context.

Once the expert knowledge has been fed into the computer it is likely to exist within a tree-like structure, with specific items of knowledge existing as axioms or rules which can be viewed as nodes within the tree. At the top of the tree is the system's 'goal hypothesis', a statement about the problem which also has probability and margin-of-error features. The expert system may have one major goal hypothesis and a number of subsidiary goals, each goal being a statement about a circumstance of the situation. Many goal hypotheses, the low-probability contingencies, will not be included: in these circumstances the system will advise the user accordingly (eg 'Ask a *real* expert!').

The intelligence of the expert system may be evaluated, perhaps frivolously, by a version of the Turing test, one of the earliest conversational scenarios. A Turing test for expert systems would have one terminal operated by the expert and one operated by the expert system: if the operator could not tell the difference, then the artificial system would be deemed truly *expert*.

Most of the operating expert systems are in the US, but as with computers in general they will become commonplace in all the advanced countries of the world. The early-1980s saw the UK's first dedicated expert systems division set up at Racal Decca, aimed specifically at the oil industry. Systems Programming Ltd has developed the rule-based technique, pioneered by Donald Michie and others at Edinburgh, to produce the Sage package announced in May 1982. Now a dozen or so Sage systems have been delivered or ordered. ICL, for example, is using Sage for projects associated with the introduction of its DM/I and Estriel mainframe computers in 1984/5. Also, a political risk system has been developed for Shell as a demonstration of Sage's capacity. ICI and BHRA Fluid Engineering are using Sage systems to exper-iment with expert systems development: ICI is using the facility to aid development of a design and consultancy aid to examine pipe stress corrosion cracking, and BHRA is developing a system to gauge flow rates and patterns inside pipes by drawing inferences from data received from sensors. SPL is also developing an open-ended question-answering system.

Expert systems, a subclass of AI, are being developed for a variety of practical purposes. Expertise is collected from human beings and fed into systems with a capacity to store and manipulate the knowledge in response to subsequent user enquiries.

FEATURES OF EXPERT SYSTEMS

General

Expert systems are being developed to solve a range of practical problems. As with fifth-generation computers they represent a departure from, in particular, traditional methods of program-ming. Expert systems have been defined as (quoted by d'Agapeyeff, 1983):

'problem-solving programs that solve substantial problems generally conceded as being difficult and requiring expertise. They are called *knowledge-based* because their performance depends critically on the use of facts and heuristics used by experts'.

The body of facts (knowledge) and the heuristics (which may be regarded as 'rules of thumb') are represented in the computer. The program uses the heuristics to operate on the stored knowledge in the light of a user enquiry, and ideally the system's reasoning can be explained to the user to indicate how a particular conclusion was reached. The British Computer Society's Committee of the Specialist Group on Expert Systems has defined an expert system as:

> 'the embodiment within a computer of a knowledge-based component from an expert skill in such a form that the machine can offer intelligent advice or take an intelligent decision about a processing function. A desirable additional characteristic, which many would regard as fundamental, is the capability of the system on demand to justify its own line of reasoning in a manner directly intelligible to the enquirer. The style adopted to attain these characteristics is rule-based programming'.

This definition emphasises rule-based programming (ie programming in logic or relational languages, such as PROLOG), allows for a wide range of applications (ie not only to consultancy functions but also to data processing and on-line control systems), and indicates the desirability of an 'explanation-of-reasoning' capability (though this does not feature in many existing expert systems). Prototype expert systems already exist in such fields as medicine, engineering and molecular genetics, and Donald Michie has mentioned a business system designed to give advice on how to reduce income tax liability. Expert systems represent a flexible approach to computer competence, drawing on specialist knowledge and exploiting various types of inference (not only deductive reasoning).

System Structure

Any expert system is characterised by three fundamental elements: the Knowledge Manager, the Knowledge Base and the Situation Model. These are shown in Figure 8.1 which includes a listing of alternative names found in the literature (following d'Agapeyeff, 1983).

The Knowledge Manager typically uses the information contained in the Knowledge Base to interpret the current contextual data in the Situation Model. Everything which is application-dependent can be kept in the Knowledge Base, allowing the Knowledge Manager to function as a multi-application tool. MYCIN, for example, advises on the diagnosis and treatment of bacterial infections (see Actual Expert Systems, below), and EMYCIN (or empty MYCIN) has been developed from the original system: a different Knowledge Base is used for different applications.

The more comprehensive the Knowledge Base, the less the strain upon the inferential logic inside the Knowledge Manager when a question has to be answered. This means that the power of the system tends to be defined according to its depth of knowledge rather than its ability to reason. In the event, however, the user will only be interested in receiving a useful response to the initial query. It may be expected that an expert system will develop – as it accumulates more expertise, either directly as new information is fed in, or indirectly as the system remembers the results of useful inferences. In addition to operating on the Knowledge Base, the Knowledge Manager will also be concerned with knowledge acquisition (ie developing the Knowledge Base), knowledge

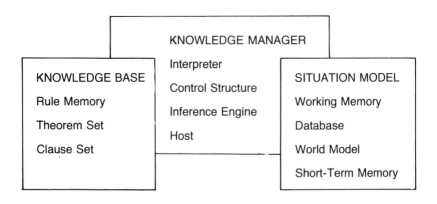

Figure 8.1   Main Elements in Expert Systems

updating (ie modifying the Knowledge Base), and providing explanations (ie explaining system features or details of operations such as inference-making). An expert system can operate at several levels – relatively superficially if a quick answer is sufficient, or more deeply if a more complex analysis is required.

Software, Inference Engines

It may be emphasised that expert systems are largely about software. (This goes nicely with Margaret Boden's 'tin-can' view of computer hardware.) Expert systems have been written in traditional languages but there is much current focus on the use of PROLOG which has also been selected, as we have seen, as the fifth-generation 'kernel' language. Languages such as PROLOG are not concerned with handling numerical quantities but with expressing relationships. This makes them highly suitable for the inference mechanisms required in both expert systems and fifth-generation computers.

The use of *rules* (eg an *if then* relationship, see Knowledge Representations, below) can serve the development of a knowledge base built up in PROLOG. In this context, no distinction is drawn between a piece of factual information (eg an item of data) and a statement rule (eg a piece of program). Both can be held in the PROLOG database and can be selected when required. PROLOG statements may be seen as constituting both the specification of the program and the program itself.

Conventional high-level languages (eg FORTRAN and COBOL) are rich in syntax but weak in semantics. This is because the languages were intended for use by professional programmers engaged in different tasks in different companies, while semantics tends to be application-specific. By contrast, expert systems are necessarily rich in semantics, and independent of machines and architectures (though particular languages are suitable for, for example, data flow architectures).

The various operating expert systems depend upon accumulating knowledge in the form of *rules*. One advantage of this approach is that the knowledge concerning the particular specialist area can be expanded incrementally; furthermore, it is in a form easily expressible by an expert. For example, the TEIRESIAS program, associated with MYCIN, collects rules from the expert, checks for rule consistency, and follows chains of reasoning to expose inadequate or inappropriate rules. A set of *meta-rules* is used to accumulate the diagnostic rules for MYCIN. The collecting of rules can be a time-consuming task. The accumulated rules and related procedures are often referred to collectively as an *inference engine* or an inference machine.

The rules comprising the knowledge base are equivalent to an application program, and they may have many different formats; the *if*-a-condition-*then*-an-action format is very common, with the *then* section able to represent inferences, assertions, probabilities, precepts, etc. The first of several conditions associated with the rule determines whether the rule is potentially valid with respect to the current state of the situation model. A rule can require that a number of conditions be satisfied before an action is authorised. The following rule, for example, is from VM (Fagan, 1980), a system for monitoring the post-surgical progress of a patient requiring mechanical breathing assistance:

> *If* the current context is 'ASSIST'
>   *and* the respiration rate has been stable for 20 minutes
>   *and* the I/E ratio has been stable for 20 minutes
> *then* the patient is on 'CMV' (controlled mandatory ventilation)

In this case, involving a transition from 'ASSIST' to 'CMV', the first condition is a state value of, and the other two measurements in, the situation model. When the rule is triggered, the context state is changed: further rules subsequently update the situation model.

A typical rule from MYCIN –

> *If* the infection is primary-bacteremia
>
>   *and* the site of the culture is one of the sterile sites
>   *and* the suspected portal of entry is the gastro-intestinal tract
> *then* there is suggestive evidence (0.7) that the identity of the organism is bacteriodes –

shows how a conclusion can be assigned a probability rating: in this case there is a 7 out of 10 chance that the conclusion is true. This follows human practice closely, where much knowledge is inexact and partial (see Uncertainties, below).

Rules, as observed, define the knowledge in the system, with meta-rules used to manipulate rules. Some systems also have meta-meta-rules; rules at the various higher levels being analogous to system software in traditional configurations. Rule-based expert systems are now relatively common (see Actual Expert Systems, below), and it has been found that good performance can be achieved in various specialist areas using 200 to 300 rules. A number of rule-independent system languages (Rita, Rosie, Age, Hearsay III) are being developed, mostly in California.

There are three broad types of system organisations for rule systems. These (following Bond, 1981) are:

— *top-down*. Here, as in MYCIN, the system sequences through top-level goals or conclusions to see if any are true. An effort is made to match the right-hand side of rules to the goal. Where a match occurs, components on the left are set up as further goals, and so on, generating a goal tree. The system pursues each goal in turn, requesting, in the case of MYCIN, clinical information as it needs it;

— *model-based*. Unlike MYCIN, this type of system organisa-tion relies upon a model of the relevant world. Rules use input data to establish and correct the model, and in particu-lar the rules chart the time development of the model. This allows predictions to be made, and the past causation to be traced. In CASNET, for example, a model of the patient's condition is built up and maintained throughout the period of treatment. Features of multiple causation can be anal-ysed and the patient's progress can be monitored and anal-ysed;

— *blackboard*. Here the rules are organised into *knowledge sources* carrying expertise in particular areas. The know-ledge sources operate, without communicating with each other, on a communal database (blackboard). The database contains hypotheses with certainty factors, and is organised to correspond to levels of data analysis. Hypotheses can be established or modified by the knowledge sources. The Hearsay speech understanding system is organised on this basis.

In addition, various other system organisations can be employed for rule manipulation. These possibilities relate directly to the four major areas being investigated in the context of knowledge representation: techniques for modelling and representing knowledge; methods enabling computers to think in natural language (since theories of inference and memory often rely on understanding how meaning is mapped onto the structure of language); techniques for deduction, problem-solving, commonsense reasoning, etc; and strategies for heuristic activity (eg allowing rapid focus on a small number of likely solutions among many possible ones). Knowledge representation and rule-based strategies are converging to enhance the competence of both the family of expert systems and the emerging fifth-generation computers.

We have seen that a variety of knowledge representation techniques can be exploited in AI programs that play games (such as chess and bridge), converse in natural language, operate robots, etc. For example, an early representation formalism was the *state-space representation*, used in game-playing and problem-solving. The structure of a problem is represented in terms of the alternatives available at each possible problem state. From any given state, all possible next states can be determined by means of *transition operators* (or *legal-move generators* in game-playing programs). One aim is to limit the number of alternatives to the best possibilities, an approach that requires programs that can reason using comprehensive knowledge about the relevant world. The overall goal is to deepen the AI programs' understanding of the problems which they are trying to solve.

Formal logic may be regarded as the classical means of representing knowledge about the world. Its progressive systematisation – from Aristotle, through de Morgan and Boole, to Frege and Russell, and then to the modern logicians – has influenced directly computer science, artificial intelligence and, in particular, the inference mechanisms being developed for expert systems and fifth-generation computers. In logic and the related formal systems, deductions can be guaranteed to be correct. The conclusions (the semantic entailment) that can be drawn from a set of logic statements are defined precisely by the laws of inference. This means, in principle, that a database can be kept logically consistent, and the derivation of new facts from old can be automated (though with a large number of facts, there tends to be an unmanageable combinatorial explosion of possibilities). In this approach, as elsewhere, there is need for more knowledge about *relevance* (eg ways of defining what facts are relevant to what situations).

The *procedural representation* of knowledge appeared in efforts to encode some explicit control of theorem-proving within a logic-based system. Knowledge about the world is contained in *procedures,* programs that know how to do particular things in well-defined situations. Here the underlying knowledge is not stated explicitly and cannot be extracted in a form that is easy for human operators to understand. Such an approach has been influential in AI research but has a number of disadvantages.

Uncertainties

Much in human problem-solving and inference is uncertain, inexact and partial (ie *fuzzy*). In many circumstances where decisions have to be made, the facts are far from precise. However, traditional logics and traditional programming have relied upon tightly-defined categories, and upon full delineations of the elements that appear in a calculation or a process. Today expert systems need a more flexible approach.

The essence of a method that can be adapted for handling inexact facts within a computer program can be found in *fuzzy set theory* (Zadeh, 1965), already mentioned. A 'model of inexact reasoning', developed in MYCIN, uses equations that perform equivalent functions to expressions belonging to fuzzy sets. Here the membership values are regarded as certainty factors which are assigned constraints. The shape of an object, for example, might be described as 'rectangular (0.6), oval (0.2) and square (0.0)', where the numbers, ranging between the binary poles of 0 and 1, indicate a degree of certainty for each quality. In contrast to what occurs in a normal database, a feature can be multivalued and indecisive.

We are all acquainted with the linguistic devices in natural language that allow subtle distinctions to be made between the features of objects. Thus we can say that a colour is 'green*ish*' or '*sort of* orange-red'. This latter may be represented in a computer program as (Colour (Red 0.7) (Orange 0.3)) or as (Colour 6000), where 6000 denotes the wavelength of the light. Shaket (1976) has described a technique able to convert physical values to certainty (membership) values. These can then be modified by linguistic devices (eg 'very', 'rather', 'sort of', etc) to cause a shift in fuzzy set values in line with what a human being might expect.

The use of fuzzy set theory and related techniques in computer programs may be regarded as one of several means of developing machine competence (in, for example, expert systems and fifth-generation computers) to approach that of human beings.

Memory Mechanisms

Expert systems are concerned with modes of information retrieval mediated by inference and other procedures. Memory considerations are crucial to these types of activity. In human beings how memory is organised is crucial to learning, the evaluation of experience, and the adoption of new behavioural patterns. We have already seen (Chapter 4) how memory mechanisms underlie most intelligent activities. It is worth emphasising how the structuring of memory is important to expert (and other knowledge-based) systems.

Work at Yale University has suggested that memory structures in human beings are subject to modification when new (unexpected or contradictory) events are experienced. Memories are linked together according to explanations and beliefs, with new connections formed when fresh information is presented to the person. In this context, R. C. Schank has proposed a theory of memory that illuminates the nature of *reminding* and other memory phenomena. Here work in AI has suggested plausible human memory mechanisms which can be explored by cognitive psychologists.

The tactic of restructuring memory in the light of new experience has already been incorporated into some expert systems. Some programs can, for example, store details of news stories and then reorganise their knowledge bases when new information is presented. In this field, as elsewhere, it is again easy to see the reciprocal influence between artificial intelligence and cognitive psychology. We may expect expert systems to become increasingly competent as they learn to model the mental processes that characterise the human specialist.

Range of Applications

There are many applications, potential and actual, for expert systems. Webster (1983) reports that the UK Department of Health and Social Security is planning to use expert systems in its social security offices: people will be able to ascertain their entitlements and how to obtain payments. In another field, the introduction of the Isolink telecommunications software modules has brought expert systems as part of office automation a step nearer. The modules allow non-technical users of the Xibus multifunction workstation – without any knowledge of protocols, addresses, procedures, etc – to access computer systems, databanks, and network services.

Most working expert systems are employed in scientific or experimental use, but today there is a clear shift towards the commercial environment (we have already cited some commercial products) and towards practical applications in such areas as education and medicine (see Actual Expert Systems, below). And many expert systems are in development: for instance, in such areas as equipment failure diagnosis, speech and image understanding, mineral exploration, military threat assessment, advising about computer system use, VLSI design, and air traffic control. Expert systems will have a role to play whenever problems have to be solved or expert advice is needed.

ACTUAL EXPERT SYSTEMS

A number of operating expert systems have already been mentioned, but it is worth considering some of these in more detail.

Medicine

Computers have been used for medical decision-making for about twenty years, employing programs that carried out well-established statistical procedures. In the main, the programs focused on the diagnostic element in consultation. Once symptoms had been presented, the computer would select one disease from a fixed set, using methods such as pattern recognition through discriminant functions, Bayesian decision theory, and decision-tree techniques. In more complex programs, *sequential* diagnosis was carried out. This involved specifying a new test for the patient in order to supplement insufficient information for a reliable diagnosis. Here the best test is selected according to economic factors, possible danger to the patient, and the amount of useful information that the test would yield.

By 1980 a wide range of diagnostic systems had been investigated. In one survey (Rogers et al, 1979), a table of 58 empirically tested computer-aided medical systems is presented (see Table 1).

In this context, computers are seen as having several inherent capabilities well suited to medical problem-solving:

— the ability to store large quantities of data, without distortion, over long periods of time;

Disease Type	Number of Studies
Endocrine, nutritional and metabolic	13
Blood and bloodforming organs	2
Mental disorders	10
Nervous system and sense organs	1
Circulatory system	5
Respiratory system	2
Digestive system	12
Genitourinary system	2
Pregnancy, childbirth and the puerperium	1
Skin and subcutaneous tissue	3
Musculoskeletal system, connective tissue	1
Symptoms, ill-defined conditions	4
Accidents, poisonings, violence	2
Total	58

Table 1   Number of Articles in Computer-Aided Diagnosis
(See bibliography in Rogers et al, 1979)

— the ability to recall data exactly as stored;

— the ability to perform complex logical and mathematical operations at high speed;

— the ability to display many diagnostic possibilities in an orderly fashion.

The accuracy of a computer-based diagnostic system depends upon many factors: the depth of the data (knowledge) base, the complexity of the diagnostic task, the selected algorithm, etc. In the Rogers et al (1979) review of applications, it was found that 60 per cent of all the diagnostic studies used an algorithm based on Bayes' theorem. Furthermore, there was a correlation between the disease class and the kind of algorithm used to make the diagnosis. Some computer-based diagnostic systems have performed better than medical consultants, and it is likely that automatic diagnostic systems will be increasingly common in various medical areas. At the same time it is important to recognise the limitations of computer-based medical systems. Moreover, attention will have to be given to the psychological elements in using a computer in the consulting room.

During the 1970s, efforts were made to apply AI techniques to problems in medical diagnosis. Again difficulties relating to inexact knowledge were evident: for instance, a particular treatment could not be guaranteed to result in a particular patient state. This situation stimulated the search for methods of representing *inexact knowledge* and for performing *plausible reasoning* (see Uncertainties, above). Diagnosis in the medical domain has been depicted as a problem of hypothesis formation, with clinical findings being used to generate a consistent set of disease hypotheses. The various expert systems devoted to medical diagnosis exploit different approaches to the task of hypothesis formation.

There are now many operating expert systems in medicine. Barr and Feigenbaum (1982) highlight typical programs (and also provide full bibliographic citations in each instance).

Attention may be drawn to MYCIN, CASNET, INTERNIST, PIP, the Digitalis Therapy Advisor, IRIS and EXPERT. In addition, there are various experimental programs being developed, including:

— PUFF, a pulmonary-function program;

— HODGKINS, a system for performing diagnostic planning for Hodgkins disease;

— HEADMED, a psychopharmacology advisor;

— VM, an intensive care monitor;

— ONCOCIN, a program for monitoring the treatment of oncology out-patients on experimental treatment regimens.

The MYCIN expert system is intended to provide consultative advice on diagnosis and treatment for infectious diseases. This is a useful facility because the attending physician may not be an expert on infectious diseases: for example, an infection may develop after heart surgery, with a consequent need for prompt treatment in conditions of uncertainty. We have already seen that medical knowledge is stored in MYCIN as a set of rules augmented by certainty factors. The factors are used to express the strength of belief in the conclusion of a rule, assuming that all the premises are true.

The MYCIN rules are stored in LISP form and individually comprise a piece of domain-specific information including an ACTION (often a conclusion) that is justified when the conditions in the PREMISE are fulfilled. Figure 8.2 shows a typical MYCIN rule (this is the LISP form of the rule given in English).

Formal evaluations of MYCIN suggest that the system performance compares favourably with that of human experts on such diseases as bacteremia and meningitis. The TEIRESIAS system operates to allow the expert to inspect faulty reasoning chains and to augment and repair MYCIN's medical knowledge. There is a consensus that the MYCIN system shows great promise.

The Causal ASsociational NETwork (CASNET) program was developed at Rutgers University to perform medical diagnosis, with the major application in the field of glaucoma. Here the disease is not represented as a static state but as a dynamic process that can be modelled as a network of causally connected pathophysiological states. The system identifies a discerned pattern of causal pathways with a disease category, whereupon appropriate treatments can be specified. The use of a causal model also facilitates prediction of the development of the disease in a range of treatment circumstances.

CASNET, adopting a strictly bottom-up approach, works from tests, through the causal pathways, to final diagnosis. Though principally applied to glaucoma, the system exhibits a representational scheme and decision-making procedures that are applicable to other diseases. Ophthalmologists have evaluated CASNET and deemed it close to expert level.

The INTERNIST consultation program, developed at the University of Pittsburgh, operates in the domain of internal medicine. A list of disease manifestations (eg symptoms, laboratory data, history, etc) is presented to the system, and diseases that would account for the manifestations are diagnosed. The program then discriminates between competing disease hypotheses. Diagnosis in the field of internal medicine can be difficult because more than one disease may be present in the same patient.

The system's knowledge of diseases is organised in a disease tree, with use made of the *'form-of'* relation (eg hepatocellular disease is a form of liver disease). The top-level classification is by organs – heart disease, lung disease, etc. A list of manifestations, entered at the beginning of a consultation, evokes one or more nodes in the tree (when a model is generated for each evoked node). In this case, a diagnosis corresponds to the set of evoked

PREMISE: (AND (SAME CNTXT INFECT PRIMARY-
                      BACTEREMIA)
                      (MEMBF CNTXT SITE STERILESITES)
                      (SAME CNTXT PORTAL GI)   )
ACTION   (CONCLUDE CNTXT IDENT BACTERIODES TALLY .7)

Figure 8.2   MYCIN Rule 050

nodes that account for all the symptoms. INTERNIST-I has been enhanced to form INTERNIST-II (which diagnoses diseases by dividing the disease tree into smaller and smaller subtrees). The system already carries more than 500 of the diseases of internal medicine, ie it is about 75 per cent complete, and practical clinical use is anticipated.

The Present Illness Program (PIP), being developed at MIT, focuses on kidney disease. The system's medical knowledge is represented in frames which centre around diseases, clinical states, and the physiological state of the patient: thirty-six such frames have been constructed to deal with kidney disease. Like INTERNIST but unlike MYCIN, PIP is designed to simulate the clinical reasoning of physicians.

Other work at MIT, carried out by the Clinical Decision Making Research Group, has been concerned with developing programs to advise physicians on the use of the drug *digitalis*. It is assumed that a patient requires digitalis: the programs determine an appropriate treatment regimen and its subsequent management in these circumstances. This approach is unusual in that it focuses on the problem of continuing patient management. This system, the Digitalis Therapy Advisor, was evaluated by comparing its recommendations to the actual treatments prescribed by human consultants for nineteen patients. On average a panel of experts preferred the recommendations of the physician, but the program's recommendations were reckoned to be the same or better in 60 to 70 per cent of all the cases that were examined.

Another medical system, IRIS, was developed for building, and experimenting with, other consultation systems. The system, designed at Rutgers University and written in INTERLISP, is intended to allow easy experimentation with alternative representations of medical knowledge, clinical strategies, etc. It has assisted in the development of a consultation system for glaucoma.

The EXPERT (expert) system, again developed at Rutgers, is aimed at helping researchers to design and test consultation models. Its development has been influenced by work in building consultation models in such medical areas as rheumatology, ophthalmology and endocrinology. (Experimental models have been developed in other areas, eg chemistry, oil-well log analysis, laboratory-instrument use, and car servicing.)

What we are seeing is a proliferation of expert system programs devoted to (first-order) diagnosis and related tasks, and to the (second-order) development of consultation systems. Whatever the task of a medical expert, it should in principle be amenable to investigation (and subsequent simulation) using expert system methods.

Chemistry

Expert systems are now finding applications in many areas of scientific research and investigation: for example, in chemical analysis, geological prospecting, and the solution of mathematical problems in engineering and physics. Computer programs have been widely applied in all the sciences for many years, but specifically AI methods have had a more limited application. In, for example, non-numeric chemical reasoning problems, these methods have been applied to:

—   identifying molecular structures in unknown organic compounds;

—   planning a sequence of reactions to synthesise organic chemical compounds.

The identification of molecular structures is important to a wide range of problems in chemistry, biology and medicine. In many cases, the sophisticated analytic methods of x-ray crystallography may not be practical, and researchers must interpret data obtained in other ways, eg via mass spectrometry. Some tests allow the chemist to discover *molecular fragments,* subparts of the molecule, from which characteristic *constraints* can be derived. These constraints are interpreted as graph features in the representation of the molecule. Some of the current AI programs use similar data to generate small subsets of the theoretically-possible structures. The identification of molecular structures, using this type of approach, is being tackled by such expert systems as DENDRAL, CONGEN, Meta-DENDRAL, and CRYSALIS. By contrast, such expert systems as LHASA, SECS and SYNCHEM are concerned with finding techniques for the laboratory synthesis of known substances.

The (Heuristic) DENDRAL program, following the formulation of the DENDRAL algorithm in 1964, identifies the possible molecular structures of constituent atoms that could account for the given spectroscopic analysis of the molecule under investigation. One main purpose of the heuristic approach was to replace the exhaustive method of the algorithm by a more economical strategy. The program achieved the objective by supplementing the DENDRAL algorithm with rules derived from expert chemists using mass spectrographic data. However, the chemists had difficulty in explicating their expertise, and the Meta-DENDRAL project was launched in 1970 to develop a means of inferring the rules of mass spectrometry from examples of molecular structures that had already been successfully analysed by human experts.

By the mid-1970s it was found that limitations on the DENDRAL algorithm allowed Heuristic DENDRAL to generate only acyclic structures (ie ketones, alcohols, ethers, amines, etc). In 1976 the CONGEN program was designed to function without the acyclic limitation.

The Heuristic DENDRAL project – from its late-1960s inception to the present – has yielded various significant results. Though the system knows far less than a human expert, it elucidates structures efficiently by searching through possibilities. Published papers (cited in Barr and Feigenbaum, 1982) have variously shown that the program can solve structure elucidation problems for complex organic molecules, and that – for example, in the analysis of mass spectra of mixtures of oestrogenic steroids – the program can perform better than human experts. DENDRAL programs have been employed to determine the structures of various types of molecules (eg terpeniod natural products, marine sterols, chemical impurities, antibiotics, insect pheromones, etc). CONGEN, deriving from the DENDRAL project, is in practical use by chemists to solve various types of problems in the elucidation of molecular structures.

Meta-DENDRAL, designed to infer the rules of mass spectrometry from known structures, learns by scanning hundreds of molecular structure/spectral data-point pairs and by searching the space of fragmentation rules for likely explanations. The rule set can be extended to accommodate new data. The proficiency of

Meta-DENDRAL can be estimated in part by the ability of a DENDRAL program using derived rules to predict spectra of new molecules. In fact the program has rediscovered known rules of mass spectrometry for two classes of molecules; and, more importantly, it has discovered *new* rules for three closely-related families of structures (the mono-, di-, and tri-keto androstanes).

The CRYSALIS expert system focuses on protein crystallography, aiming to integrate various sources of knowledge to match the crystallographer's performance in electron-density-map interpretation. (This would fill an important gap in the automation of protein crystallography.) The concept of an electron density map generally denotes some pictorial representation (eg a three-dimensional contour map) of electron density over a certain region. The skilled crystallographer can study such a map to discover features allowing him to infer atomic sites, molecular boundaries, the polymer backbone, etc. In due course a structural model can be built to conform to the electron density map. Automation of this task requires a computational system that could generate, display and test hypotheses.

In CRYSALIS the hypotheses are represented in a hierarchical data structure, with knowledge sources able to add, change and test hypothesis elements on a 'blackboard' (see Knowledge Representation, above). The system can at present only perform a portion of the total task of interpreting electron density maps. The knowledge base is relatively small, but this is expanding and a capability is envisaged for the complete interpretation of medium-quality medium-resolution electron density maps.

We have already mentioned the three major organic synthesis programs. LHASA (Logic and Heuristics Applied to Synthetic Analysis), maintained at Harvard, is the earliest. This system yielded SECS (Simulation and Evaluation of Chemical Synthesis), now being developed at the University of California. SECS extended the LHASA approach by more extensively exploiting stereochemical and other types of information. The third major program of this sort, SYNCHEM (SYNthetic CHEMistry), is being developed at the State University of New York.

The main item of knowledge in chemical synthesis is the chemical reaction. Here a rule describes a) a situation in which a molecular structure can be changed, and b) the change itself. The programs use knowledge of reactions to design a synthesis route from starting materials to target molecule. In summary:

— the LHASA knowledge base, a set of procedures, contains very sophisticated chemistry knowledge but is difficult to update;

— the SECS knowledge base, carrying about 400 separate transforms, allows new transforms to be added without the need for program changes;

— the SYNCHEM knowledge base includes a library of reactions and commercially-available starting compounds. Chemists can modify the knowledge base without reprogramming.

Computer-aided chemical synthesis is regarded as a potentially valuable new facility for chemists, whether engaged in research or industrial manufacturing. A key factor in expert systems devoted to organic synthesis is how much they know about chemical reactions. The three main synthesis programs have all demonstrated their ability to find synthetic routes for organic materials.

Mathematics

MACSYMA, originally designed in 1968, is a large computer system used to assist mathematicians, scientists and engineers in tackling mathematical problems. It accepts symbolic inputs and yields symbolic outputs, and, in addition to its algebraic-manipulation competence, it includes a large numerical subroutine library. Today MACSYMA, running on a DEC KL-10 at MIT and accessed through the ARPA Network, is used by hundreds of US researchers. Many workers from government laboratories, universities and private companies spend much of every day logged in to the system.

As with many other expert systems, the performance of MAC-SYMA relies upon an extensive knowledge base. This enables the interactive system to perform more than 600 different types of mathematical operations, including differentiation, integration, equation solving, matrix operations, and vector algebra. MAC-SYMA currently comprises about 230,000 words of compiled

LISP code and a similar amount of code written in the special MACSYMA programming language.

Many of the system algorithms were known before the development of MACSYMA, while others evolved during the system research. AI helped to frame the environment in which MACSYMA was born, and various AI-related capabilities are currently being developed in the system (for example, a new representation for algebraic expressions and a knowledge-based 'apprentice').

Geology

Various computer-based systems are being developed to aid geologists engaged in exploration tasks. One of the best known of these systems is PROSPECTOR, being developed at SRI International to help geologists working on problems in hard-rock mineral exploration. (PROSPECTOR made news in 1982 when it was given the same field study data about a region in Washington State as that used by experts in a mining company. The system concluded that there were deposits of molybdenum over a wide area. The geologists disagreed but when exploratory drilling was undertaken PROSPECTOR was found to be right.)

The user provides PROSPECTOR with information about a region (eg data on rock types, minerals, alteration products, etc), whereupon the program matches the information against its models. Where necessary, PROSPECTOR asks the user for more information to enable a decision to be reached. The user can intervene at any stage to provide new data, change existing information or request an evaluation from the system. A sophisticated inference network is used to control PROSPECTOR's reasoning, with network nodes corresponding to various geological assertions (eg *There is alteration favourable for the potassic zone of a porphyry copper deposit*). Rules are employed to specify how the probability of one assertion affects the probability of another (these inference rules are analogous to the production rules used in MYCIN).

A geologist using PROSPECTOR prepares a model as an inference network. The current system contains five different models (developed in cooperation with five consulting geologists):

Koroko-type massive sulphide, Mississippi-Valley type lead/zinc, type A porphyry copper, Komatiitic nickel sulphide, and roll-front sandstone uranium. These models are collectively represented by 541 assertions and 327 rules. Using the models and input data, the system is able to adjust the probability of hypotheses in changing circumstances.

The five models have only recently been developed to the point when useful geological evaluations could be made. And many further models are needed for extensive coverage of the full prospecting domain.

Education

Computer technology has been applied to education since the early-1960s, with applications in such areas as course-scheduling, test-grading, and the management of teaching aids. One aim of CAI (Computer-Aided Instruction) research has been to build instructional programs that incorporate course material in lessons that are optimised for each student. In the Intelligent CAI (ICAI) programs that began to emerge in the 1970s, course material was conveyed independently of teaching procedures – to enable problems and comments to be generated differently for each student. Today, AI is influencing the design of programs that are sensitive to the student's strengths and weaknesses, and to the preferred style of learning.

Early research on ICAI systems tended to concentrate on the representation of the subject matter. Attention may be drawn to such benchmark efforts as: SCHOLAR, a geography tutor; SOPHIE, an electronics troubleshooting tutor; and EXCHECK, a logic and set theory tutor. These systems have a high level of domain expertise, which allows them to be responsive over a wide spectrum of interactive problem-solving situations. Other expert educational programs are:

— WHY, which tutors students in the causes of rainfall, a complex geographical process that is a function of many variables. This system exploits 'socratic tutoring heuristics' and is able to identify and correct student misconceptions. WHY began as an extension of SCHOLAR;

— WEST, described as a program for 'guided discovery' learning. The system, deriving from a board game, assumes that a student *constructs* an understanding of a situation or a task, the notion of progressively corrected misconceptions being central to this assumption. The learning student interacts with a 'Coach';

— WUMPUS, which again uses game techniques to teach a mixture of logic, probability, decision theory and geometry. In one version, the coach is WUSOR-II, a system that involves the interaction of various specialist programs. Four basic modules are used: Expert, Psychologist, Student Model, and Tutor. The system is recognised to be a useful learning aid;

— GUIDON, a program for diagnostic problem-solving which uses the rules of the MYCIN consultation system. A student engages in a dialogue about a patient suspected of having an infection, and learns how to use clinical and laboratory data for diagnosis purposes. This system goes beyond responding to the student's last move (as in WEST and WUMPUS) and repetitive questioning and answering (as in SCHOLAR and WHY);

— BUGGY, designed to identify a student's basic arithmetic misconceptions. The system can provide an explanation of why a student is making an arithmetic mistake. Experience has indicated that forming a model of what is wrong can be more difficult than performing the task itself. BUGGY can be used to train teachers to diagnose errors in the way that students work.

The above programs are essentially *teaching* systems, and other programs are available to assist *learning by doing*. Emphasis may be given to effective 'learning environments' such as LISP-based LOGO (and its most celebrated application, turtle geometry), the message-passing SMALLTALK (and its extension, THING-LAB), and the DIRECTOR animation system. Here powerful programming-language features are used with sophisticated graphics facilities. AI has contributed to expert systems in the educational environment, as elsewhere.

Today there is frequent reference (eg in Roberts and Park, 1983) to *intelligent computer-assisted instruction* (ICAI) systems which allow enhanced flexibility in the learning environment. We may expect such developments to continue in the years to come. A central aim is to provide the student with a natural learning environment allowing one-to-one relationships, as occur traditionally between students and tutors.

Design and Fault Diagnosis

There is increasing scope for expert systems in a wide range of design and fault diagnosis applications. One aim is to 'pit knowledge against complexity, using expert knowledge to whittle complexity down to a manageable scale' (Stefik and de Kleer, 1983). In this way, expert systems can be used in, for example, digital system design, one of many possibilities being researched at Digital Equipment Corporation (DEC) and elsewhere. With one experimental expert system, transistor size in integrated circuits is determined and circuit parameters such as load and capacitance are defined. In 1978 DEC began work, in conjunction with Carnegie-Mellon University, to develop a knowledge-based program called XCON for configuring VAX-11/780 computers. EURISTO, an AI program used to configure naval fleets in competition games, has recently been employed to search for useful microcircuits structures made possible by multilayer fabrication technology.

At the Massachusetts Institute of Technology the Artificial Intelligence Laboratory has been experimenting with expert systems for many years. Systems such as EL and SYN help designers to analyse and synthesise analogue circuits. The PALLADIO system, developed at Zerox and Stanford University, is intended to help designers to experiment with new methodologies. A designer can discover gaps in the knowledge base by applying it to his own design, allowing subsequent modifications (to both knowledge base and design) to be made.

Thomas et al (1983) describe how expert-system methods are now being applied to the synthesis and design of VLSI circuits for computers and other systems. Emphasis is given to the development of the CMU-DA system which uses a behavioural statement to propose functional block components and alternate block interconnections that will implement the specified behaviour. A computer-aided design environment is being developed to aid the automatic synthesis of the behavioural and functional block levels of design. Here programs such as DAA and EMUCS are used for synthesis purposes. Using another approach, an expert system called SMX-Cogitor has been developed in Sweden to perform structural analysis and to check programs and problem solutions.

The computer retrieval incidence bank (CRIB) is one of several expert systems designed for computer fault diagnosis (see description in Hartley, 1984). The system can be used for diagnosis of faults in both hardware and software, and relies upon a knowledge base of simple factual information that can support the diagnostic task. The system designers investigated 1) the knowledge required by an engineer to find faults, and 2) how this knowledge is used by a skilled human practitioner. CRIB, now comprising a configuration of four programs, is regarded by its designers as a prototype for better systems. Another fault diagnosis system, FALOSY (FAult LOcalisation SYstem, described by Sedlmeyer et al, 1983) is used specifically for program debugging. More ambitiously, the New Medius expert system, from IAL Data Communications, is intended to locate network faults and (when system development is complete) to fix them by organising repairs.

The task of fault diagnosis requires the application of a set of techniques to a particular subject domain. It is easy to envisage a general fault-diagnosis system that can be bolted on to different knowledge bases. However, most research into expert-system fault diagnosis has focused on particular subject areas: computer circuits, electrical wiring, network connections, etc. Pratt (1984) describes a computerised diagnostic system using AI techniques plus the expertise of an engineer to diagnose faults in locomotives. The system, developed by the General Electric Company's New York Corporate Research and Development Centre, will soon be widely used in railroad service depots throughout the United States. A central aim is to give the system humanlike modes of reasoning.

Business and Offices

Expert systems will become increasingly available to business and office workers, just as they will emerge in the factory and engineering environments. For example, the Financial Advisor (based on the Nexus expert system) has been launched by Helix Products and Marketing as an aid for businessmen and other professional people. Financial Advisor offers advice on business management and helps to diagnose financial problems. Other Helix systems are Investment Advisor (to analyse investment possibilities) and Car Advisor (for those people deciding how to buy a car and which one), with other areas – such as personnel, loan administration, tax policies, etc – already targeted for expert-system development.

TAXADVISOR is an expert system (described by Michaelsen and Michie, 1983) designed to make tax planning recommendations for businessmen and other users. The system asks questions about a client's current wealth, and then gives advice to help him maximise his wealth within certain constraints. Another system, AUDITOR, developed at the University of Illinois, has been developed to help auditors assess a company's allowance for bad debts. Auditing information was assembled in rule form, initially for use on the AL/X system developed at the University of Edinburgh. Other systems are TAXMAN (for evaluating the tax consequencies of certain types of proposed business reorganisation) and CORPTAX (to advise the user about redemption policies).

A wide range of expert systems are being developed by DEC for in-house use. These include XSITE (an expert site planner's assistant), IMACS (to aid manufacturing), ISA (to aid scheduling), IPMS (to aid project management), XPRESS (to aid the refining of organisational procedures) and ILRPS (to aid long-range planning). XSEL, designed to help the salesperson develop system orders, was introduced for use in the US in September 1983 with the aim of extending its usage worldwide in 1984/5. This system interfaces between sales and engineering, addresses the problems of incorrect sales configuration, unprepared sites and unrealistic delivery estimates. DEC, with 22 departments working on AI projects, aims to encourage development of both commercial and in-house expert systems.

In a telecommunications development relevant to the office worker, Xionics has introduced the Isolink modules to allow non-technical users of the Xibus multifunction workstation to access computer systems, databanks, networks and other facilities. This type of development will be influenced by progress in expert systems.

Expert-Ease

Work at Edinburgh University, under the direction of Donald Michie, has led to the development of Expert-Ease, an expert-system generator for the IBM Personal Computer. This system is a micro version of ACLS, a minicomputer program developed using an algorithm known as Quinlan's ID3. Expert knowledge is entered in the form of examples whereupon Expert-Ease produces the rules that apply and presents them as a decision tree. Descriptive tags can then be attached to the keywords to provide a system that can be used by non-experts. In effect this allows the user to build his own expert system by incorporating whatever specialist knowledge is required.

The systems generated by Expert-Ease can individually involve up to 250 questions, each having up to 31 possible conditions or answers. The human expert must enter all the questions and answers, and it is certainly possible for an incompetent expert to create an incompetent expert system. Already about 60 users have acquired early versions of Expert-Ease, and in 1984 faster, easier-to-use versions of the program have been launched. It is thought that the system will appeal to hospitals, government departments and companies wishing to develop effective enquiry systems.

At the heart of Expert-Ease is the ACLS (Analogue Concept Learning System) software, developed by Intelligent Terminals Ltd and supplied to Export Software International to be incorporated into a commercially attractive package. Using (mainly) induction, the package can generate an effective, albeit limited, system to provide helpful advice to computer-naive users. Expert-Ease exemplifies a current trend in the development of expert-system facilities – the movement towards economic systems for maximum market appeal (see also Expert Systems and Micros, below).

Other Expert Systems

There are now commercial expert systems for dozens of different subject areas. In addition to the systems already profiled in this section we can mention:

MOLGEN, for the analysis and synthesis of DNA

DART, for diagnosing computer system faults

SPEAR, for analysing computer error logs

SACON, for assisting in structural engineering

AGE, for developing expert systems

LDS, for making legal (product liability) decisions

CALLISTO, for modelling large manufacturing projects

AIRPLAN, for planning military air-traffic movement

HYDRO, for solving water resource problems

WAVES, for advising on seismic data analysis

GENESIS, for planning gene-splicing experiments

CADUCEUS, for medical diagnosis

TATR, for tactical air targeteering

This list, which could easily be extended, shows the range of expert systems currently functioning and under development. There can be little doubt that this trend will continue in the future. As topics such as knowledge representation and the heuristics of effective problem solving are better understood, and as experience of functional expert systems grows, it will be increasingly possible to provide computer-based advisory facilities in any specific subject domain. Wherever human expertise exists it will be possible, in principle, to model this competence in artificial systems. It is not difficult to imagine how the increasing availability of low-cost expert systems will impinge on the professional employment scene. As one consequence, specialists in every field will experience the employment insecurities, caused by increased automation, that factory workers have known for decades.

EXPERT SYSTEMS AND MICROS

We have seen that Expert-Ease (above) has been designed to run on the IBM PC (it requires 128K random-access memory and one disk drive, with two disk drives recommended), and the size of the microcomputer market indicates a massive commercial arena for expert systems – if they can be trimmed down as necessary.

No-one doubts that small computer systems will proliferate throughout the world in the years to come. In 1982, represented as a 'banner year' for small systems, no less than 1,440,000 such devices were sold worldwide, with more than one million sold in the US alone (a 70 per cent leap over 1981 sales). One prediction (in the journal *Byte*, January 1983) suggests that in the year 1991 around eleven million personal computers will be sold throughout the world. Colin Crook, managing director of Zynar, has suggested that by that time there will be 200 to 400 million personal computers in the world – and many of them will be powerful machines, programmed in PROLOG, and able to run hosts of expert systems.

Personal computers, a central element in the Japanese fifth-generation programme, will be parallel processing machines, individually based on as many as 32 processors, carrying 10 megabytes of memory, and working at a rate of 10 million instructions per second. It has been suggested (eg by Philip Hughes, chairman of Logica and a member of the Alvey group) that smart applications for personal computers may be the best way for the UK to exploit developments towards fifth-generation systems. Clive Sinclair has already hinted at the possibility of offering expert system packages for the Spectrum and later on for the ZX83 home system (this latter based on the ICL-Sinclair workstation). Logic Programming Associates has sold more than 100 copies of a MicroProlog compiler. It may be expected that the expert systems that will be of most use to personal computer users will be in the areas of problem-solving, question-answering and education.

At the same time the difficulty of putting really useful expert systems onto microcomputers should be noted. The PROSPECTOR expert system, for example, written in a dialect of LISP called INTERLISP, has program listings running to more than 300 pages of source code. This requires a DEC mainframe to run. Faced with this weight of software, 'most micros would curl up and die' (Webster, 1983).

It is likely that expert system versions will soon be developed for microcomputers (much as a rudimentary ELIZA is available for an Apple II), but without the high-level competence of the fully-fledged systems. A version of PROLOG is being developed for the Sinclair Spectrum, and parallel developments will encourage the emergence of micro-based expert systems.

Already efforts are being made to reduce the size of existing expert systems to allow them to run on microcomputers. For example, the PUFF medical expert system has been rewritten in Basic, allowing the system to be adapted for use on microcomputers. (PUFF works with compilations of test results and individual medical histories to produce diagnoses.) At the same time there is a general feeling that true expert systems have not yet appeared on micros. Alexander Jacobson, president of Inference of Los Angeles, a company that develops expert systems for the IBM 370 XT and Apollo minicomputers, has declared: 'We don't think any expert system worthy of the name can run on a micro'. A significant future is envisaged for knowledge-based microcomputer systems, but at present few micros claim to use the AI techniques (eg inference) that characterise genuine expert systems. (Some AI methods are used in micro-based games.) Watt (1984) highlights a few current attitudes and research activities that bear on the relationship between artificial intelligence and microcomputers (attention to Expert-Ease).

It is important to remember the characteristic features of the typical expert system. A specialised knowledge base is crucial, as is the power to 'think about' the stored knowledge to yield new conclusions. Micros may boast fancy interactive software which does not nonetheless constitute an expert system. In scaling down a mainframe-based expert system for use on micros, its central AI features may be emasculated. It is still fair to say that no fully-fledged expert system has been produced for microcomputer users.

SUMMARY

This chapter has profiled the typical expert system, with attention to structure, software, AI aspects, range of applications, and other aspects. Expert systems give a high profile to efforts among AI researchers to develop computer-based systems that exhibit humanlike characteristics. The human expert is a manifest example of specialist competence rooted in knowledge and thinking ability. A computer system that effectively models this competence is clearly intelligent.

We see a rapidly expanding range of expert systems: no area of human expertise is immune to the explorations of the knowledge engineer. It is not difficult to envisage the day when computer-based systems will be scientists, mathematicians, social advisers, engineers, managers, lawyers, etc. People should not be complacent about the effects of expert-systems development on human activity in society. It is even *intended* that human specialists should be replaced by machines. Thus Sy Bosworth, at a recent Softcon press conference (at which Expert-Ease systems were displayed), declared: 'Some people may be making mistakes continuously. Those so-called experts can and should be replaced'. He cites doctors whose faulty medical diagnoses cause unnecessary surgery or who run 20 tests when 14 of the tests are superfluous – 'We want to replicate the knowledge of the truly expert, with fewer wrong decisions and wrong moves' (quoted by Mace, 1984).

Expert systems are probably the most significant practical implementation to date of AI techniques. Developments in this area will influence the shape of fifth-generation systems and many other emerging advanced computer-based facilities. Moreover, expert systems represent one of the most successful realisations of efforts to model areas of human competence. Again this is a field that will see rapid development in the years to come.

9 Other AI Products

INTRODUCTION

Research into artificial intelligence is now yielding a wide range of marketable products, and this is a circumstance that will further boost investment in AI work. It is one thing to devise clever AI programs in the laboratory, quite another to translate these into commercial products that stimulate further research funding. We have seen the growing range of expert systems, but these only represent the most obvious AI sector with commercial potential. There are many other types of AI products that will increasingly influence the shape of the marketplace.

The first AI products have been recognised as the harbingers of a new generation of computer hardware and software. Computer companies are now recognising the importance of AI and some of these firms are already deeply involved in this area. For example, the Japanese government and Japanese computer companies are already three years into the AI-linked fifth-generation computer project, and this activity has stimulated responses from US and European firms (in Britain the Alvey initiative has already begun funding a range of projects in the field). British industry is sponsoring the Turing Institute, set up in 1984 with the involvement of Strathclyde University (the initial sponsors include ICL, Sinclair Research, Thorn-EMI, Shell Oil research laboratories and government agencies). It is intended that the institute will focus on research into such topics as automatic programming, knowledge-based systems and advanced robotics.

The Paris-based Schlumberger company – with research

laboratories including the Fairchild Research Laboratory in Palo Alto, California, and Schlumberger-Doll Research in Ridgefield (Conn.), and with a major equity holding in Bolt, Beranek & Newman (Cambridge, Mass) – has made a large commitment to AI. ICL (Britain), Siemens AG (West Germany) and Compagnie Machines Bull (France) have formed a joint research institute for knowledge processing. Work in AI is being conducted in the USSR and Eastern Europe (Hungary exports an AI programming language – see *Electronics*, 6/10/83, p 110).

AI products are now available in such areas as robotics, office automation, aids for the disabled, system development, man/machine interfaces (for example, using speech input/output), military equipment, etc. This chapter profiles a few of these product areas, emphasising that AI will increasingly shape the marketplace in areas where computers already have a presence. Often AI systems simply add a level of competence to existing computer-based facilities. For example, the Judgment-Space ('J-Space') document-indexing-and-retrieval system, a product of Information Access Systems Inc, helps professionals to retrieve relevant documents (one user has commented: 'It's uncanny the way it goes and retrieves just what you want'). In another field, that of robot technology, it is AI (plus, for example, the provision of new types of sensors) that is moving a wide range of products from one generation to the next. And in other areas (eg the development of prosthetic devices for paraplegics), work in AI is resulting in types of products that are entirely new (representing a revolutionary rather than an evolutionary development).

The products mentioned in this chapter are only a few of the ones currently being marketed in Europe, the US and elsewhere. It is hard to think of an area that will not be affected by the increasing availability of AI-based systems. In one estimate (cited in *Mini-Micro Systems*, June 1984, p 85), the AI market should triple to $220 million in 1985 and grow to $8 billion by 1993.

ROBOTS

General

Robots can serve as a high-profile representation of applied AI technology. All types of robotic systems nicely manifest the behavioural characteristics that allow us to make judgements as to system competence, flexibility, intelligence, etc. Not all robots are intelligent: the vast majority of working robots are programmed to work in predetermined paths, and are incapable of independent initiatives. It is part of the contribution of AI research to render robotic systems intelligent, ie able to respond in adaptive ways in changing environmental circumstances.

Robot intelligence may be provided by means of computers separate from the device and linked to it (and possibly also to other robots) by cables, or by 'on-board' distributed computers organised to control various robot functions (eg interpretation of sensory data, limb movement, etc). Melear (1983), for example, describes how an 8-bit CMOS microcomputer designed for industrial control is used to supervise three microprocessors responsible for controlling the movements of an industrial robot. In another example, a modular microprocessor-based controller is used to drive a robot (designated 'Smart'). The Smart robotic system is produced by Comau SpA, a subsidiary of Fiat, and it is capable of flexible expansion to meet the requirements of a user who may already have a computer-based automation facility. The development of AI for robotic devices is largely a question of how computer intelligence can be used to extend the sensory and manipulative competence of robots in a working environment.

We may expect the functional flexibility of robots to be expanded by various technological developments, apart from those in computer-based AI. For example, it has been suggested that particular communication innovations may make it easier to link robots to powerful computer facilities. Researchers at the University of Sydney are experimenting with infra-red light as a means of eliminating the expensive and cumbersome computer cable connections. In particular, robots would be rendered much more mobile. (Dr Ian Parkin, senior lecturer, has observed: 'One could imagine mobile robots wearing infra-red hats that would enable them to communicate with each other and their main computer'.) In such a fashion, robots could be 'freed' to implement an enhanced range of behavioural options specified by powerful computer software.

It is clear that a number of parallel technological developments will converge to enhance robot intelligence. Sensor technology, manipulator mechanics, communications, materials technology, computer technology – all will contribute to the evolution of robot competence in a wide range of industrial, commercial, service and domestic environments.

The AI Impact

There is increasing reference in the research literature, advertising copy and new books to the 'intelligent robot'. Thus a report prepared by Technical Insights Inc (Fort Lee, New Jersey) and the SEAI Institute, called *The Intelligent Robot*, includes a section on 'Artificial Intelligence and Robotics' (the advertising blurb runs: 'Robots are becoming smarter everyday. That means some significant opportunities for you. It also represents some significant competitive dangers if you ignore the intelligent robot'). In the late 1970s it was becoming increasingly obvious that AI could be linked to robotic devices to produce a higher level of automation in the industrial context. Garrett (1978) discusses how a 'natural approach' to artificial intelligence can help to develop the competence of working robots. In particular, he focuses on a modular approach to intelligence ('It is this approach, that of designing robots in a modularised, increasing levels of distributed intelligence manner, which I believe will provide the most systematic, and hence rewarding, understanding of the nature of intelligence'). Here again is the evident reciprocal influence between AI research and efforts to understand natural intelligence. Witkowski (1980) suggests that one of the reasons for applying artificial-intelligence techniques to robotics is to gain a better understanding of the essential nature of intelligence. He emphasises that AI is a mix of ideas – about perception, problem solving, abstraction, generalisation, skilled action, learning, memory, etc – and points out that various robotic devices demonstrate 'at least one or two' of these faculties to a limited extent. For example, Edinburgh University's Freddy robot system was programmed to construct small wooden toys from a disorganised heap of component parts.

The impact of AI on robots has been to enlarge robot competence in the specific functional areas where robot performance is important. For instance it is increasingly important for robots to be able to see machined components and to manipulate them for assembly and other purposes. (Robots are not yet interested in writing Japanese haiku but there is one, Cubot, who can solve Rubik's Cube – using a camera eye, manipulator fingers and a computer brain – in less than four minutes.) We may expect robot intelligence to evolve in various specific areas of robot activity: robots will thus tend to develop as factory workers and domestic slaves, rather than as poets or painters – even though writing poetry and painting pictures are of interest to AI workers. Hence the type of robot intelligence that develops will be largely conditioned by the sorts of tasks upon which robots, as seen by human beings, should be appropriately engaged. Already we *could* equip robots with a wide range of rudimentary AI faculties but there is usually little point. Anyone wishing to play chess against a machine is generally satisfied with a computer. Robot chess players are available but the addition of artificial fingers, eyes, etc is usually seen as a needless complication.

Robot Senses

We have seen (Chapter 6) the importance assigned in AI research to machine vision, and what is true of the sense of sight is true also of the other senses, albeit to a lesser degree. The sighted robot is a rapidly evolving species, and other senses – some of them akin to existing biological faculties and some not – are also developing for various purposes. By the 1980s, as we have recorded, many computer-based vision systems were already being introduced for inspection and assembly tasks (see, for example, Agin, 1980); and it was soon clear that vision facilities would help the 'factory of the future' to become a reality (Meyer, 1983). It is now clear that machine vision – for robots and other devices – will become a major growth area in the years ahead.

Robot vision has already been successfully implemented in many commercial systems and others are under development. Toshiba, for example, has produced a sighted robot which carries two TSR-500V robot arms which interact with one another to duplicate the complex motions of a human production line worker. In this system a camera acts as a visual sensor. One application is in the soldering of wiring terminals to components in the base of an electric fan. A tiny camera lens is mounted in the middle of the robot hand ('gripper') and is used to identify the position of the wire and terminal. The robot picks up a wire that has been identified by colour, and then places it at the correct terminal. Another robot moves across to solder the wire in position.

In 1984 the Sumitomo company launched an image recognition device 'virtually as good as the human eye'. This product, the IS32 Optic RAM, has evoked much interest at Micron Technology in Idaho. Joyce Popp, marketing manager, has commented that the Sumitomo product is similar to the Micron Eye, which has been marketed for two years ('We aim to investigate the product of the Japanese company thoroughly'). Two hundred complete Micron Eye kits and 500 Optic RAMs are now being shipped every month, but it has proved necessary to vet companies carefully before delivery ('This is inevitable with a revolutionary product such as this, which is way ahead of anything else in robot vision').

The Sumitomo Electric Industries device is controlled by a 16-bit microcomputer which is also used as a robot brain. The image recognition device, a principal selling point of the new robots, can show objects in the form of contour lines for focusing and confirmation by the human operator. It is also able to recognise areas of medium intensity, an ability that is rare among industrial robots. Other robots have been able to cope only with high-intensity images.

Robots with sight and touch have now been working in industry for several years, and one estimate (cited by Braggins, 1984) suggests that 25 per cent of robots in the US will be sighted by 1990. Braggins describes the Meta Machines vision-guided welding torch, which includes a combined welding head and camera with integral laser light source. This system has been developed by Oxford University's Robotics Group.

Other vision robots are being used by General Motors at a foundry at St. Catherines, Ontario. Here three Cincinnati Milacron robots are guided by a vision system developed by the GM Technical Centre at Warren, Michigan. The foundry is a harsh place for a sensitive vision system but the Cincinnati units have been working five shifts on, one off, since 1981. Other vision systems have been developed by ASEA, International Robomation/Intelligence, Control Automation, Robotic Vision

Systems, etc. The sighted robot will be commonplace in factories and elsewhere in the years ahead.

One of the main reasons behind vision research is the desirability of enabling robots to cope with variations in the automatic-assembly process. If parts are not precisely positioned a robot without vision will have difficulty picking them up for assembly. General Electric of America has produced the BinVision system which enables a GE robot to locate and pick up randomly-orientated, overlapping parts from a container or other work area. The system can accommodate four cameras and so deal simultaneously with four different parts.

There are various limitations on the scope of the BinVision system. For example, it cannot handle parts weighing more than 8 kg and their shapes should resemble cylindrical, spherical or billet type solids with a length-to-diameter ratio greater than or equal to 2:1. Moreover they must be rigid, opaque as opposed to translucent, and have a reflective surface. Special lighting conditions are required. By contrast, a special ASEA system has been designed to operate in normal conditions.

The new ASEA system (suitable for materials handling, simple assembly and various integrated operations) can be programmed for particular tasks. A part is placed beneath the camera and the vision system displays the part's contours on a VDU. The operator then moves a cursor around the shape that the robot should memorise. The shape is then programmed, a facility that allows the system to accommodate many different types of components. The system has been tried out in ASEA Control in Vasteras, Sweden, which produces low-voltage switchgear and control equipment.

The robot uses vision to identify which of twelve parts it is to handle, whereupon it selects an appropriate program and gripper. Then a part is picked up and the flash removed, after which the item is placed on a conveyor or a pallet, depending upon the type of part. The system is expected to run without human intervention for many hours. This facility, like the GE development, provides customers with a fully integrated seeing robot. Another vision system has been supplied by British Robotic Systems Ltd (BRSL) for the 600 Group's flexible manufacturing system (FMS). One application of the BRSL Autoview Viking vision system is in sorting car cooling hoses. This is a typical use of the increasingly common robotic vision facilities.

Senses other than vision are also being developed. There is speculation about robots that can hear, smell, touch, etc. Tactile (touch) sensory devices – using artificial skin, pressure pads or other touch elements – are already being used in the operational environment. For example, tactile sensitivity can be used to control gripper pressure, so that delicate objects are not crushed. Various vision and tactile systems were described at the 3rd Robot Vision and Sensory Controls conference (1984) in America.

The question of force sensing of gripper jaws can be tackled in various ways. In one system a tactile pad has 64 individually-sensed points, and is able to sense the shape of a formed washer pressed against it by a robot arm. Magnetostrictive sensors are being researched as a means of providing tactile sensitivity on a hard surface, but they are limited to use with nonferromagnetic objects. Philips and RCA have developed force sensors to enable robots to assemble TV yokes onto tubes (and loudspeakers onto mounts). The provision of tactile and other sensors is one of the ways in which robots are being rendered more intelligent. Central to this type of development is the availability of adequate software that can interpret the output from the sensors and generate the appropriate signals to complete the cybernetic control loop.

Factory Robots

An increasing range of jobs are being tackled by computer-controlled robots and other automated systems. (Sometimes the applications are unexpected: for example, there has been much recent attention – in both the general and technical press – to the development of a robot sheep-shearer. By 1984 this robot had sheared more than 200 sheep, and, according to its inventors at the University of Western Australia, broken the skin only a dozen times.) Most functional robots are being produced for work in factories, and increasingly such devices are being given a degree of intelligence. Thus Keller (1983) remarks (in an article entitled 'Clever robots set to enter industry en masse'): 'The ever-improving price-performance ratio of computing power, coupled with the incorporation of other advanced electronic technology, is generating *robots that are capable of acquiring enough knowledge to stand alongside many of their human rivals*' (my italics).

The new robots have sensors of various types, localised closed-loop control, off-line programming, and screen simulation capabilities. With such provisions the robots can adjust to their surroundings and accommodate different operational requirements when performing a task. Such abilities mean that robots can cope with increasingly difficult tasks: for example, in assembly operations where components need to be manipulated with precision. Sophisticated sensors will increasingly be used to give robots an adaptive potential in the factory environment. Artificial skin may be made out of conductive rubber or PZT, a piezo-electric ceramic from Vernitron Corp. (in Bedford, Ohio), or a lattice of sensitive 'nerve endings' may be set in a substrate and connected to a robot gripper. Carnegie-Mellon is developing a tactile sensor based on polyvinylidene fluoride (PVF_2) film which can be metalised on both sides for electrical contact. An alternative approach is to use strain gauges to provide tactile sensitivity. The provision of greater degrees of 'sensor intelligence' in robots means that conveyor systems and fixturing devices can be simplified: the robot can detect the variations in, for example, how components are delivered, and then take appropriate actions.

Work on vision systems tends to focus on a few basic methods: for instance, on light striping and triangulation to provide depth information. With light striping, light patterns are flashed onto a subject by a light source, whereupon the reflected patterns are detected by a camera. From camera position and pattern deformation, triangulation equations can be used to determine how an object is changing in shape along three axes. In a system developed by Digital/Analog Design, use is made of eight stages of image processors plus two stages of ALUs (arithmetic/logic units) to recognise an image having 256 levels of grey. An IBM Personal Computer is used as a controller.

The progressive incorporation of sensor provisions in factory robots may be regarded as one of the main processes contributing to enhanced intelligence in automated systems. Controllers for robots tend to work independently, oblivious to changes in the environment, but sophisticated controllers (for example, the AI32 from Automatix Inc. (Billerica, Mass) can simultaneously control several robots and other pieces of equipment. Such controllers can be linked to sophisticated sensors to provide a closed-loop supervision of industrial processes. Again the available software will determine the scope of an intelligent robot complex in this sort of manufacturing environment. Conventionally a robot is taken through a task sequence by a human operator, or off-line programming can be achieved using a personal computer. Moreover new languages are being developed to aid the provision of intelligent software for robot systems.

A central aim of AI research is to enhance the autonomy of local systems, ie to render human intervention unnecessary. At the same time there is a requirement for the various manufacturing elements (robots, machine tools, conveyors, etc) in the factory cell to communicate with each other so that tasks are scheduled effectively. Schreiner (1983) describes how a robot can be integrated with other robots and computers to function in a manufacturing work cell. Here attention is given to the Intelledex Model 705 robot which is capable of managing in-circuit pc board testers as elements in an integrated facility.

Eventually AI systems will control the entire flow of information in the manufacturing environment. Computer-based facilities will plan, schedule and control the entire production process, monitoring and updating inventories, designing products, finding and repairing faults, reading reports to adjust production according to market and other needs, etc. It is obvious that such a situation will have profound consequences for staffing, manufacturing philosophies and the allocation of funding.

Personal Robots

The idea of the personal robot, an uncomplaining 'domestic slave', has long excited science fiction writers. Today there is growing discussion about the feasibility of such a device, and working models are already appearing in various countries. The British company Visual Machines, for example, has launched a family of personal robots, TOPO and friends, that use technology developed at Manchester University. Such devices have extremely limited abilities and there is debate as to how competent personal robots will become in the future. Professor Keith Rathmill of the Cranfield Robotics and Automation group has dismissed talk of robot butlers as 'misleading science fiction poppycock', suggesting that robots have no future in the home. But Ira Pence, Unimation's vice president of engineering, has declared: 'We can create a home robot now. Only the high costs are holding us back' (quoted by Bruno, 1984). This observer suggests that robots will be cooking and cleaning homes within five years. There is much speculation about how such a robot would behave.

The robot would be controlled by simple verbal comands to activate preprogrammed routines. Since the robot would be mobile it would carry sensors so that it could negotiate the various items and obstacles in a room. Its mobility would be rendered intelligent by providing the robot with a floor plan of the user's house, and the device would have learning ability – if the furniture was moved around, the robot would be able to reprogram itself to cope with the new geometry. Pence suggests that Unimation will produce a prototype home robot in 1986 to commence deliveries in 1988. Again the main obstacle is price: today a sophisticated home robot could be built for around $250,000. Unimation aims to reduce this figure to about $12,000. But already various companies are producing domestic robots with various limited powers.

The RB5X device, from Colorado-based RB Robots, is equipped to feel its way around a room, sweeping the carpet at the same time. And devices from companies such as Heath and Androbot are also helping to launch the era of the personal robot. Androbots, using the Topo technology developed at Manchester University, run round on two motor-driven wheels – until an obstacle is encountered, when a stress detector senses the overload on the motor and switches it off. The Heath robot, Hero 1, uses a similar mechanism to control the pressure exerted by its hand.

B.O.B. (Brains on Board), known as Bob, is Topo's smarter brother. This device uses two on-board microprocessors and can synthesise speech using a prerecorded set of digitised phrases. Infra-red sensors in B.O.B.'s head cause him to follow human beings, ultrasonic sensors causing him to avoid obstacles in his path. The aim is to provide plug-in boards to provide eyesight, a voice-recognition facility, etc. The software is expected to include

AndroSentry, a home security/alarm package, and AndroFridge, which will allow the robot to fetch a can of beer (or whatever) for the human user. B.O.B. uses fold-down panels to support items being carried, but as yet the robot has no hands or grippers.

The Heath Hero 1 personal robot has voice-recognition and voice-synthesis capabilities (with a pitch control that helps the synthesiser create a humanlike inflection). The voice-recognition faculty is, in AI terms, extremely primitive. No effort is made to understand the various parts of speech. Instead the unit simply counts the number of syllables. If Hero is required to fetch a can of soft drink he will respond just as effectively to hearing '7-Up' as to hearing 'Mountain Dew'.

Both Topo and Hero need the assistance of human beings when the robot batteries run low. The human user has to plug the robots in to the mains for recharging, usually overnight. By contrast, RB5X, already met, will search for a suitable battery charger and plug himself in when necessary. RB5X can also include an on-board speech synthesiser, and an arm provides a Hero-like competence. Another company, Robotics International, is developing the Genus robot, a device that will include an extendable arm which can retract inside its body. It is expected that Genus, expected to sell for around $5000, will be able to perform a wide range of domestic chores, including vacuum cleaning and fetching and carrying.

The limitations on the competence of personal robots mirror the rudimentary state of AI. For example, it is an easy matter for a human being to recognise the difference between a dirty plate and a clean one, prior to washing up – but a robot would have great difficulty in making this simple distinction. The development of effective cognitive software will be necessary before domestic robots will be able to perform most of the tasks that people find simple and mundane.

Professor Les Valiant of Harvard University, speaking at a meeting (February 1984) on mathematical logic and programming languages, arranged by the Royal Society, presented a light-hearted scenario to indicate AI difficulties facing the domestic robot – you are about to leave for a holiday and the robot is to be in charge of the house for a month, but suddenly you remember that you have not told the robot to feed the dog; worse still, you have not even taught it how to recognise the dog ('you might not be able to write a program for recognising a dog'). This again emphasises the importance of cognitive abilities (learning, understanding, perceiving, etc) for the performance of simple tasks.

The provision of cognitive competence in artefacts depends upon an adequate solution of problems in knowledge representation and other areas. Valiant believes that propositional calculus, the simplest form of symbolic logic, is more powerful than many people believe, and that it can be used to facilitate the programming of robots to carry out learning and other sophisticated cognitive tasks. For example, a program written to enable the robot to recognise a dog will use elements with which the robot is already familiar (eg dog = animal AND NOT cat AND has four legs). Other considerations – for example, the use of the 'conjunctive normal form' (cnf) and 'oracles' – are also relevant to learning capacities in domestic and other types of robots (see discussion in Durham, 1984).

The development of domestic robots will depend in large part on the development of effective cognitive software. General progress in AI will feed into the domestic arena as it will feed into every other social sector. It is perfectly possible to devise domestic robots that rely on preprogramming to perform well-defined simple tasks. Such robots would not be intelligent: the contribution of AI in this field is to hasten the day when domestic robots, like robots in other areas, will be able to perform difficult tasks in a flexible and resourceful fashion – to behave in fact like human beings.

Robots Tomorrow

Robots in the future will have a range of competence and abilities. It will not be necessary for all robots to have a flexible, all-round, high level of intelligence. 'Dedicated' robots will be assigned specific abilities and they will not require skills that are irrelevant to their immediate tasks. At the same time, there are obvious advantages in the idea of a general-purpose robot, a surrogate human being, that can be effortlessly switched from one task to another. Progress in AI will determine the levels of competence in the smartest robots.

It is important not to overestimate the competence of today's robots. In the words of one observer (Davies, 1984), 'today's robots are still largely blind, dumb and daft'. Nonetheless they are still finding important applications in many fields. For example, effective robots arms are being added to the chairs of the disabled, though again there are often prohibitive cost factors. With enhanced sensors and on-board data processing power, industrial robots are becoming more flexible in the working environment. And experimental devices are progressively exploiting the latest AI work.

In 1983 the Japanese Ministry of International Trade and Industry (MITI) began a project to develop robots capable of working in environments that might be unsafe for human beings. The project was designed to accomplish:

— the development of special-purpose robots, for operation in nuclear plants and undersea research stations, to provide disaster relief, equipment and facility maintenance, and advanced assembly;

— the development of generic technologies such as mobile mechanisms, manipulators, sensors, control systems, and system totalisation;

— the promotion of international research cooperation through the advancement of robotics.

It is recognised that the robots of the 1980s, the first perception and problem-solving robots, represent the first generation of intelligent robots. The MITI plan involves developing technology, with a high level of AI input, to produce second- and third-generation robots. Unimation and other US companies, aware of the high-profile Japanese projects, have their own far-reaching R & D programmes.

The MITI robot project will draw on the results of research into fifth-generation computers (see Simons, 1983). Advanced robotics systems will be developed from existing work in such areas as pattern recognition, learning and problem solving. In addition, the Japanese Mechanical Engineering and Electrotechnical Laboratories are researching visual and tactile sensors, manipulators, multiped walking systems, flexible hands with fingers, etc. One aim is to develop a competent robot for hazardous environments. Such a robot will have:

— a high degree of mobility;

— flexible arms with multiple joints and fingers;

— an element of autonomous control ability.

Such robots will also have a highly developed sensory capability. They will be sighted and will have tactile senses. In addition they will be equipped to detect radioactivity, infra-red emissions, ultrasonic waves, millimeter electromagnetic waves, and toxic gases (ie they will also be able to smell, hear and perform sensory activities beyond the competence of human beings). Another aim will be to modularise the robot systems, so that they can be configured for different applications. The various research projects (see Togai, 1984) are focusing on:

— *mobility*. Mechanisms will be developed to allow robots to climb stairs, proceed over rough terrains, climb walls and trenches, etc, variously exploiting the advantages of wheeled and legged locomotion;

— *manipulation*. Devices will possess a high degree of freedom and special geometries. They will be sensitive to pressure, torque and other factors. Systems will need to be highly reliable, some possessing fault-tolerance and diagnostic features;

— *sensors*. We may expect the development of real three-dimensional vision, tactile (shear, contact, force and displacement) sensors, and systems for exploiting other electrical, acoustic and radiation phenomena;

— *autonomous control*. Robots will have autonomous navigation systems to allow for intelligent mobility, and autonomous facilities will allow local decision-making to cope with new environmental circumstances;

— *telepresence*. Robots will be required to feed back telepresence effects to the human operator. This technology will require to measure human movement, to configure anthropomorphic systems, and to provide suitable telepresence effects;

— *power systems*. It will be necessary to reduce the size of existing power units, to make them more energy-efficient, and to make them robust for harsh environments. Miniature actuators and high-torque power units will be developed;

— *control languages*. 'Friendly' robot control languages will be developed to improve the man/robot interfaces. At the same time robots will increasingly be able to understand natural language.

These various areas of interest – not an exhaustive list – are important in Japanese robot research projects, and they are mirrored in the research programmes being conducted in Europe and the United States. The nature of the research schemes helps to indicate the sorts of features that we can expect in tomorrow's robots. These devices will be highly mobile, possessed of a wide range of senses (some of them unknown in biological species), and able to take decisions, solve problems, learn and perform other cognitive tasks that depend upon success in basic AI research.

Intelligent robots in the years ahead will be active in virtually every industrial and social arena, including some areas that would be highly dangerous to human beings (where, for example, there is great heat, toxic chemicals or radioactivity). Robots will progressively evolve to narrow the gap between themselves and human beings, at the same time developing a range of nonhuman, but highly useful, abilities.

SPEECH SYSTEMS

We have highlighted (in Chapter 7) the importance to AI researchers of speech and language understanding systems. Already a number of products are available that exploit AI work to provide language and speech competence in various ways. By 1980 it was obvious that speech-recognition systems, for example, were a practical possibility for various applications. Welch (1980), as one observer, saw voice control in the industrial environment as particularly useful where:

— the worker's hands are occupied;

— mobility is required during data entry;

— the worker must keep observing a display, an optical device, or an object to be tracked;

— the environment does not permit keyboard use.

Such requirements stimulated the development of voice-recognition systems for use in industry and other sectors.

One successful voice-recognition system is Logos, developed by Logica using techniques designed by the Government's Joint Speech Research Unit (JSRU). This system, designed for continuous speech, can cope with vocabularies of several hundred words, and even includes features to reduce the system's sensitivity to variations in microphone position and background noise. This type of system can be used in the industrial environment, offices, schools, hospitals, etc. It is one of a growing range of voice-recognition facilities that will influence the shape of work practices in many different contexts.

By 1984 the Alvey Programme included a voice-driven word processor as a pilot study for demonstrator projects. Plessey aims in this context to develop a word processor that could be activated by spoken commands, with the objective of launching a cost-effective commercial product. Increasingly, voice input is being regarded as a realistic option for various types of computers and computer-based systems. For example, the Texas Instruments Professional computer offers an effective voice-recognition capability. Texas calls this a 'speech and telephone management' facility, since it sees the market for the device as wider than mere voice recognition. A voice-recognition board creates characters exactly as though they had been entered via a keyboard.

As with most other voice-recognition systems, the Professional requires the user to train the computer to recognise his or her voice inputs. Key words or phrases can be employed to trigger commands; for example, to control cursor movement. The company reckons that the system improves its performance over time, as a series of voice prints is built up. The competence of the Professional, albeit limited to a narrow range of commands, indicates that voice input is likely to become a favoured man/machine interface approach.

AI AND LISP PRODUCTS

Now that artificial intelligence is emerging from the laboratory onto the marketplace, a growing range of AI-based products is available. Some of these are systems uniquely equipped to run the mainstream AI languages, such as Prolog and Lisp. Manufacturers are offering a growing spectrum of machines that can exploit the features of such languages in various ways. Xerox, for example, has produced a commercial Lisp machine and other manufacturers are developing similar products. The first Lisp machines appeared in 1981 and Xerox quickly saw the relevance of such devices to the rapidly expanding office-automation market. In mid-1981 the Xerox Dolphin system was launched as the 1100 'scientific information processor'; and Symbolics Inc and Lisp Machine Inc produced the LM-2 and the Lisp Machine, respectively. Later Xerox also launched the Dandelion/1108 and the Dorado/1132 systems. These were some of the first products in the expanding AI machine market.

In 1983 Lisp Machine Inc. (LMI) announced the Lambda system, a successor to CADR; and Symbolics Inc. began shipments of the Symbolic 3600 LISP machine. The LMI president, F Stephen Wyle, has emphasised that by-products of AI research have resulted in such things as timesharing, networking, windowing, and some powerful software tools ('In a sense, LISP machines are another such product – a tool developed for AI researchers that is usable for purposes not necessarily associated with AI'). Abe Hirsch, Symbolics product line manager, has pointed out that out of the first forty customers for the 3600, there were forty different applications – including video game design, artificial vision and computer-based training.

The market for the LMI and Symbolics LISP machines is expected to grow as AI spreads into commercial applications. Foster (1983) cites an estimate that the market for LISP machines will reach $100 million within two years, encouraged by the growing demand for AI-based products of all kinds. Another estimate suggests that the market for AI hardware, software and services will reach $8 billion within ten years (see also Manuel, 1983).

The main advantage of the various Lisp machines – from Xerox, LMI and Symbolics – is that they enable large powerful programs (that could not be handled by traditional methods) to be written, tested and modified. But traditional computers cannot support Lisp, which is why there is a need for hardware and software to integrate Lisp-based systems in existing computer environments. In this way, there can be productivity increases for the development of a wide range of software systems, and AI can be brought to existing computer systems. Creeger (1983) describes how the design of Lisp machines is conducive to these objectives.

We see the emergence of a new class of computers, geared to the specific AI features of the Lisp language (and its dialects, eg Interlisp) and designed to aid the development of both AI-related products and other computer-based facilities. The Lisp machines are essentially seen as development tools with particular qualities defined by the character of the Lisp formalism: for example, there is less emphasis on numeric computation, more on the manipulation of 'objects' or 'concepts'. This gives Lisp machines a power of thought analogous, but not equivalent, to that of human beings. The *range* of systems development is enhanced and, for the first time, a new family of computers can exploit particular *cognitive features* to accelerate the emergence of new systems.

MILITARY DEVICES

It is inevitable that there should be military interest in new AI products. New developments in computing have generally been stimulated by military funding – from the early days of Bletchley code-breaking and ENIAC (computing artillery firing charts) to the modern military interest in systems based on gallium arsenide (GaAs), perhaps because this substance, in contrast to silicon, is highly resistant to the effects of radiation. Today there is considerable military interest in expert systems, in computer-controlled weaponry, in the various implementations and ramifications of the automated battlefield.

Today there is military involvement in robotics (Corrado, 1983), in voice recognition and synthesis (Iversen, 1980), and in the various ways in which 'smart' weapons can be designed to cope with the variations that may occur in an operational situation. Computer-based systems are already involved in war gaming, and in assessing early warning data. Again the AI influence is significant in various areas. The US Army Corps of Engineers is investigating automated mapping applications. Robert Leighty, head of the Engineer Topographic Laboratories (ETL), has commented: 'The ETL approach to AI applications will be to keep the human in an interactive system and to provide AI modules, which will improve total system performance. Evolution of this system will reduce the need for human interaction and result in automated systems of the future' (quoted by Corrado, 1983).

ETL is also investigating what is termed 'cartographic license' – the need to adjust or omit map features to enable an intelligent cartographic system to perform effectively. The development of this type of system meshes with another project – the design of a Robotic Reconnaise Vehicle (RRV), able to analyse terrain characteristics. The Navy is also researching intelligent vehicles. Current US Department of Defence projects include: advanced hand/eye/arm manipulators, microelectronics systems and control algorithms for cooperative robots, three-dimensional and stereo vision systems, acoustic sensors, autonomous and semiautonomous navigation systems, survivable power sources for adverse circumstances, etc. Attention is also being given to how AI research can be exploited in crisis-warning systems, natural-language understanding, expert systems, automated mission planning and scheduling, automated programming, etc.

There is a growing military investment in AI and robotics for both industrial and battlefield applications. The massive funding available in this context is one guarantee that AI work will develop rapidly in the years ahead. One concept entertained by the US Department of Defence is that it would be useful to create a robotic workforce for its future industrial needs: the 'workerless' factory, it seems, is not just a commercial requirement but also a military need. There is growing debate about the wisdom of military reliance on massive computer systems that no-one really understands. It is likely that this debate will be stimulated further by the increasing involvement of artificial intelligence in military matters.

SUMMARY

This chapter has drawn attention to a few AI products (Chapter 8 dealt with expert systems). A situation is developing in which AI, albeit in a rudimentary form, is beginning to encroach on one area after another – much as the broader phenomenon of computing itself has done over the last two or three decades.

Robot technology is a crucial area that will increasingly feel the impact of AI research. Robotic systems will gradually acquire mobility, sophisticated senses, and the ability to navigate, solve problems and take decisions in an autonomous fashion. In the years to come we will find intelligent robots in factories, offices, hospitals, schools, prisons and the home (the domestic appliance manufacturers Electrolux and Qualcast are considering the possibility of producing robot vacuum cleaners and grass cutters) The growing impact of AI on the development of robot intelligence will be aided by progress in such areas as microelectronics, mechanical and electrical engineering, and sensor technology.

Other AI products are emerging in the man/machine interface arena, with speech input/output facilities and software that embodies cognitive attributes. New computer systems that can run the mainstream AI languages – LISP and PROLOG – are now commercially available, and these will dramatically affect the evolution of both new AI systems and new computer-based facilities in other areas. As two examples, LISP machines are now being produced by various manufacturers, and PROLOG is being made available (sometimes as a dialect) for a widening range of machines, including microcomputers. For instance, a Sinclair brochure declares: 'Specially adapted for your ZX Spectrum, micro-PROLOG offers a fascinating insight into a language which will play a vital role in future computer developments.' The use of such a language can facilitate dialogue, concerning everyday concepts and ideas, between the computer and the human user.

AI products will be available in one social sector after another. Both professional and non-professional employees will come to rely upon them, much as today they rely upon the telephone or the electronic calculator. Inevitably the military uses of artificial intelligence – in expert systems, 'smart' weapons, voice recognition, strategy planning, etc – will continue to attract massive funding. AI is now in a dramatic transition phase, between the laboratory and the marketplace (and the marketplace includes all those areas where goods are bought and sold). It is obvious that artificial intelligence is no longer merely a fanciful but socially inconsequential topic: it is beginning to acquire a strategic importance in commerce, industry and national security.

10 The Future

INTRODUCTION

To some extent this book has already talked about the future, discussing past and present ideas but also indicating what we may expect in the years ahead. Artificial intelligence is very much an emerging discipline (or complex of disciplines): it is still not uncommon for the basic AI philosophy to be ridiculed ('artificial intelligence is a contradiction in terms'), yet the first AI products are already on the market.

Many different disciplines (Specific Development Areas, below) are contributing to the development of AI systems. Perhaps most importantly, AI researchers are aiming to design systems that will duplicate (mimic, simulate) modes of thought and behaviour that are characteristic of human and nonhuman animals (there is also some evidence that a plant, *mimosa pudica*, can learn from experience and that trees can communicate using chemical messengers). AI researchers have often drawn on what is known about, for example, human problem solving to devise problem-solving artefacts. The importance of findings in biology and psychology to progress in artificial intelligence is likely to continue in the future.

BIOLOGY AND PSYCHOLOGY

Artificial intelligence is essentially concerned with building characteristically biological and psychological features into machines. Norbert Wiener, four decades ago, showed that closely analogous mechanisms of communication and control can be found in both biological and artificial systems. The resulting science of *cybernetics* – concerned with such activities as information handling, feedback and adaptation – is equally focused on animals and machines. Today, developing this approach, the *cognitive sciences* variously embrace the mutually influential disciplines of psychology, linguistics, computer science, neurophysiology and artificial intelligence. AI researchers will continue to learn from new insights into human cognitive psychology, and the psychologists will derive benefit from the various psychological modelling methods developed in artificial intelligence.

AI systems will evolve to duplicate an ever widening range of human mental and behavioural characteristics and processes (see The Spectrum of AI, below). We can speculate about when general-purpose AI systems will have a range of competence equivalent to that of the average human being.

SPECIFIC DEVELOPMENT AREAS

Many different disciplines and technologies are converging to give impetus to the development of artificial intelligence. These highly-interlocking trends may be broadly considered as *technologies* and *theoretical concerns*.

Technologies

Microelectronics technology currently underlies the whole of computer science. Here circuits are traditionally silicon-based, though new devices are being produced and investigated that depend upon substances such as gallium arsenide and indium phosphate.

At the same time there is increasing speculation about computer systems that could be based on *protein molecules* or on *optical components* to achieve higher levels of data storage and performance.

New *supercomputers* are already being produced to give, through (for example) *parallel* or *data flow architectures*, vastly increased levels of computational power.

In robotics there is significant progress in such areas as *sensor technology, mechanical engineering*, and the provision of robust miniaturised *power supplies*.

Theoretical Concerns

The various AI processes depend upon the formulation of appropriate *algorithms, heuristic procedures* and techniques of *knowledge representation* for particular tasks.

Again, findings in *biology* and *psychology* are highly relevant to these sorts of considerations. For example, an understanding of aspects of *visual perception* (eg the phenomenon of stereoscopy) can lead to the development of computational algorithms for artificial systems.

At the same time, *methods of logic* – ranging from first-order *propositional calculus* to *fuzzy* and *nonmonotonic formalisms* – will be investigated to aid knowledge representation and methods of inference in artefacts.

Progress in such areas will influence the evolution of *programming languages* able to cope with concepts and ideas rather than simple 'number-crunching' tasks. *Logic programming*, as exemplified by such AI languages as Lisp and Prolog, will increasingly affect the shape of software in the years to come.

Moreover, progress in such fields as *linguistics* and *epistemology* will influence the scope of *language understanding* and *concept formation* in machines.

We see a host of abstract disciplines combining to shape the character of artificial intelligence in the years ahead. Progress in these various fields will inevitably expand the spectrum of AI.

SPECTRUM OF AI

The spectrum of AI has traditionally been concerned with a group of well defined cognitive functions – memory, learning, problem solving, decision-making, language understanding, game playing, visual perception, etc. In the future these various activities will become more sophisticated and, in many ways, more humanlike. These processes represent, in some sense, an initial phase of AI evolution. Increased understanding of the various theoretical concerns and technological progress will combine to extend the spectrum of AI to such phenomena as intuition, creativity and emotion. There are already, for example, many cognitive theories of emotion (see K. T. Strongman, *The Psychology of Emotion*, Wiley, 1978), which implies that emotion could be effectively modelled by appropriate information-processing mechanisms. *There is in principle no human faculty that could not be built into artificial systems.*

SUMMARY

This chapter has briefly indicated some of the technological and theoretical concerns that will continue to influence the evolution of AI systems in the modern world. Over and above such matters are the central sociopolitical questions that will determine the survival of the human race: nuclear war would contribute little to the development of AI systems on earth, though it is not impossible that they would have a hand in its instigation. Such cataclysms apart, progress in artificial intelligence can be predicted with confidence, granted adequate funding appropriately directed. The interest of modern governments, as shown in recent years, and the perennial commercial concern of companies suggest that this funding will be available.

Appendix 1

REFERENCES

References

CHAPTER 1

Allport D A, Patterns and actions: cognitive mechanisms are content-specific, in Guy Claxton (ed), *Cognitive Psychology: New Directions,* Routledge and Kegan Paul, 1980

Boden M, *Artificial Intelligence and Natural Man,* Harvester Press, 1977

Burt C, The evidence for the concept of intelligence, *British Journal of Educational Psychology,* 25, 1955, pp 158-177

Cattell J McK, Mental tests and measurement, *Mind,* 15, 1890, pp 373-380

Dockrell W B (ed), *On Intelligence,* Methuen, London, 1970

Ebbinghaus H, Über eine neue Methode zur Prüfing geistiger Fahigkeiten und ihre Answendung bei Schulkindern, *Zeitschrift für Angewandte Psychologie,* 92, 1897, pp 331-334

Ernst G W and Newell A, *GPS: A Case Study in Generality and Problem Solving,* Academic Press, New York, 1969

Gagné R M, *Essentials of Learning for Instruction,* Dryden Press, Illinois, 1974

Gagné R M, *The Conditions of Learning,* Holt, Rinehart and Winston, 1977

Galton F, *Hereditary Genius: an Enquiry into its Laws and Consequences,* Macmillan, London, 1869 (reprinted by Watts and Co., 1950)

Galton F, *Inquire into Human Faculty and its Development*, Macmillan, New York, 1883

Hofstadter D R, *Gödel, Escher and Bach: An Eternal Golden Braid*, Harvester Press, 1979

Hunt E, Lunneborg C and Lewis J, What does it mean to be high verbal?, *Cognitive Psychology*, 1975, pp 194-227

Mason B, Intelligence tests for computers, *Personal Computer World*, December 1982, pp 134-135, 137

Miles T R, Contributions to intelligence testing and the theory of intelligence. I. On defining intelligence, *British Journal of Educational Psychology*, 27, 1957, pp 153-165

Miller G A, *Psychology: the Science of Mental Life*, Hutchinson, London, 1964

Pyle D W, *Intelligence*, Routledge and Kegan Paul, 1979

Sloman A, *The Computer Revolution in Philosophy: Philosophy, Science and Models of Mind*, Harvester Press, 1978

Spencer H, *Principles of Psychology*, Williams and Norgate, London, 1870

Surya, The age of reason, *Personal Computer World*, Volume 7, Number 3, March 1984, pp 216-218

Weizenbaum J, *Computer Power and Human Reason*, W H Freeman, San Francisco, 1976

CHAPTER 2

Boden M, *Artificial Intelligence and Natural Man*, Harvester Press, 1977

Feigenbaum E A and McCorduck P, *The Fifth Generation: Artificial Intelligence and Japan's Computer Challenge to the World*, Michael Joseph, 1983

George F H and Humphries J D (eds), *The Robots are Coming: The Implications of Artificial Intelligence Developments*, NCC Publications, 1974

Hofstadter D R, *Gödel, Escher, Bach: An Eternal Golden Braid*, Harvester Press, 1979

Raphael B, *The Thinking Computer: Mind Inside Matter*, W H Freeman, San Francisco, 1976

Simons G L, *Towards Fifth-Generation Computers*, NCC Publications, 1983

Sloman A, *The Computer Revolution in Philosophy: Philosophy, Science and Models of Mind*, Harvester Press, 1978

Turing A M, Computing machinery and intelligence, *Mind*, Volume LIX, Number 236, 1950

Winston P H, *Artificial Intelligence*, Addison Wesley, 1979

CHAPTER 3

Allport D A, Patterns and actions: cognitive mechanisms are content-specific, in Guy Claxton (ed), *Cognitive Psychology: New Directions*, Routledge and Kegan Paul, 1980

Chomsky A N, *Syntactic Structures*, Mouton, The Hague, 1957

Hunt E, What kind of a computer is man?, *Cognitive Psychology*, Volume 2, 1971, pp 57-98

Lindsay P H and Norman D A, *Human Information Processing*, Academic Press, 1977

Masuda R and Hasegawa K, A design approach to total sensory robot control, *Sensor Review*, January 1982, pp 20-24

Mayer R E, *The Promise of Cognitive Psychology*, W H Freeman, San Francisco, 1981

Miller G A, Galanter E and Pribram K H, *Plans and the Structure of Behaviour*, Holt, Rinehart and Winston, New York, 1960

Neisser U, *Cognitive Psychology*, Appleton-Century-Crofts, New York, 1967

Newell A, Shaw J C and Simon H A, Elements of a theory of human problem solving, *Psychological Review*, 65, 1958, pp 151-166

Piaget J, *The Construction of Reality in the Child,* Basic Books, New York, 1954

Posner J, Boies S, Eichelman W and Taylor R, Retention of visual and name codes of individual letters, *Journal of Experimental Psychology Monographs,* 79 (1, Pt 2), 1969

Pylyshyn Z, Complexity and the study of artificial and human intelligence, in John Haugeland (ed), *Mind Design: Philosophy, Psychology, Artificial Intelligence,* Bradford Books, Vermont, 1981

Quastler H, Studies of human channel capacity, in E C Cherry (ed), *Information Theory: Proceedings of Third London Symposium,* Butterworth, London, 1956

Reitman J S, Information processing model of STM, in D A Norman (ed), *Models of Human Memory,* Academic Press, London and New York, 1970

Sampson G, *The Form of Language,* Weidenfeld and Nicholson, 1975

Sloman A, *The Computer Revolution in Philosophy: Philosophy, Science and Models of Mind,* Harvester Press, 1978

Strongman K T, *The Psychology of Emotion,* John Wiley, 1978

Winograd T, Computer memories: a metaphor for memory organisation, in C Cofer (ed), *The Structure of Human Memory,* W H Freeman, San Francisco, 1975

CHAPTER 4

Allport D A, Patterns and actions: cognitive mechanisms are content-specific, in Guy Claxton (ed), *Cognitive Psychology: New Directions,* Routledge and Kegan Paul, 1980

Barr A and Feigenbaum E A, *The Handbook of Artificial Intelligence,* Volume 1, Pitman, 1981

Boden M, *Artificial Intelligence and Natural Man,* Harvester Press, 1977

Cohen P R and Feigenbaum E A, *The Handbook of Artificial Intelligence,* Volume 3, Pitman, 1982

Ernst G and Newell A, *GPS: A Case Study in Generality and Problem Solving,* Academic Press, New York, 1969

Funt B V, Analogical modes of reasoning and process modelling, *Computer,* October 1983, pp 99-104

Narendra K S and Mars P, The use of learning algorithms in telephone traffic routing – a methodology, *Automatica,* Volume 19, Number 5, 1983, pp 495-502

Nau D S, Decision quality as a function of search depth on game trees, *Journal of the Association for Computing Machinery,* Volume 30, Number 4, October 1983, pp 687-708

Raphael B, *The Thinking Computer: Mind Inside Matter,* W H Freeman, San Francisco, 1976

Robinson J A, A machine-oriented logic based on the resolution principle, *Journal of the ACM,* 12, 1965, pp 23-41

Voysey H, Machine learning waits in the wings, *Computing,* 29 March 1984, p 36

Winston P H, *Artificial Intelligence,* Addison Wesley, 1979

CHAPTER 5

Barr A and Feigenbaum E A, *The Handbook of Artificial Intelligence,* Volume 1, Pitman, 1981

Brachman R J, Fikes R E and Levesque H J, Krypton: a functional approach to knowledge representation, *Computer,* October 1983, pp 67-73

Dahl V, Logic programming as a representation of knowledge, *Computer,* October 1983, pp 106-110

Feigenbaum E A and McCorduck P, *The Fifth Generation,* Michael Joseph, 1984

Israel D J, The role of logic in knowledge representation, *Computer,* October 1983, pp 37-41

Langley P, Representational issues in learning systems, *Computer,* October 1983, pp 47-51

Lindsay P H and Norman D A, *Human Information Processing: An Introduction to Psychology*, Academic Press, 1977

Minsky M, Framework for representing knowledge, *Mind Design*, Bradford Books, 1981; article first published 1974

Mylopoulos J, Shibahara T and Tsotsos J K, Building knowledge-based systems: the PSN experience, *Computer*, October 1983, pp 83-88

Newell A, Production systems: models of control structures, in W G Chase (ed), *Visual Information Processing*, Academic Press, 1973

Nilsson N, *Problem Solving Methods in Artificial Intelligence*, McGraw-Hill, New York, 1971

Sloman A, *The Computer Revolution in Philosophy: Philosophy, Science and Models of Mind*, Harvester Press, 1978

Winston P H, *Artificial Intelligence*, Addison-Wesley, 1979

Woods W A, What's important about knowledge representation?, *Computer*, October 1983, pp 22-27

Zadeh L A, Fuzzy sets, *Information and Control*, 8, 1965, pp 338-353

Zadeh L A, Commonsense knowledge representation based on fuzzy logic, *Computer*, October 1983, pp 61-65

CHAPTER 6

Boden M, *Artificial Intelligence and Natural Man*, Harvester Press, 1977

Braggins D, Vision systems: helping robots to see things our way, *Machinery and Production Engineering*, 18 April 1984, pp 38-39, 41

Cohen P R and Feigenbaum E, *The Handbook of Artificial Intelligence*, Volume 3, Pitman, 1982

Havens W and Mackworth A, Representing knowledge of the visual world, *Computer*, October 1983, pp 90-96

Henkel T, Vision systems still in infancy but promising, *Computerworld*, 26 March 1984, p 15

Jain R and Haynes S, Imprecision in computer vision, *Computer*, August 1982, pp 39-47

Myers W, Industry begins to use visual pattern recognition, *Computer*, May 1980, pp 21-31

Onda H and Ohashi Y, Introduction of visual equipment to inspection, *The Industrial Robot*, September 1979, pp 131-135

Poggio T, Vision by man and machine, *Scientific American*, April 1984, pp 68-78.

Powley C, Bad light won't stop recognition, *Machinery and Production Engineering*, 2 November 1983, pp 33-34

Raphael B, *The Thinking Computer: Mind Inside Matter*, W H Freeman, San Francisco, 1976

Sloman A, *The Computer Revolution in Philosophy: Philosophy, Science and Models of Mind*, Harvester Press, 1978

Szuprowicz B, Boom times predicted for artificial vision industry, *Computerworld*, 26 March 1984, p 105

Yachida M and Tsuji S, Industrial computer vision in Japan, *Computer*, May 1980, pp 50-63

CHAPTER 7

Barr A and Feigenbaum E A, *The Handbook of Artificial Intelligence*, Volume 1, Pitman, 1981

Boden M, *Artificial Intelligence and Natural Man*, Harvester Press, 1977

Brightman T and Crook S, Exploring practical speech I/O, *Mini-Micro Systems*, May 1982, pp 291-305

Durham T, Interpreting the job of the translators, *Computing*, 24 November 1983, p 25

Frude N, *The Intimate Machine*, Century, 1983

Fry D B, Speech reception and perception, in J Lyons (ed), *New*

Horizons in Linguistics, Penguin Books, 1970

Henthorn K S and Dawson I, An application of speech recognition and synthesis, *Journal of Microcomputer Applications*, 6, 1983, pp 295-305

Iverson R D, Arnott P J and Pfeiffer G W, A software interface for speech recognition, *Computer Design*, March 1982, pp 147-152

Kirvan P F, Conversing with computers, *Data Processing*, March 1984, pp 49-51

Lashley K S, In search of the engram, *Symposia of the Society for Experimental Biology*, 4, 1950, pp 454-482

Miller G A and Johnson-Laird P N, *Language and Perception*, Cambridge University Press, 1976

Osgood C E, Where do sentences come from?, in D D Steinberg and L A Jakabovits (eds), *Semantics: an Interdisciplinary Reader in Philosophy, Linguistics and Psychology*, Cambridge University Press, 1971

Raphael B, *The Thinking Computer: Mind Inside Matter*, W H Freeman, San Francisco, 1976

Rouvray D and Wilkinson G, Machines break the language barrier, *New Scientist*, 22 March 1984, pp 19-21

Sampson G, *The Form of Language*, Weidenfeld and Nicholson, 1975

Schalk T B and van Meir E L, Terminals, listen up, speech recognition is a reality, *Computer Design*, September 1983, pp 97-102

Scheibe K E and Erwin M, *Journal of Social Psychology*, 108, 2, 1980, p 103

Tennant H, Natural language processing and small systems, *Byte*, June 1978, pp 38-54

Trevarthen C, The psychology of speech development, *Neurosciences Research Program Bulletin*, 12, 1974, pp 570-585

Webber B L, Logic and natural language, *Computer*, October 1983, pp 43-46

Young J Z, *Programs of the Brain*, Oxford University Press, 1978

CHAPTER 8

Addis T R, Expert systems: an evolution in information retrieval, *Information Technology: Research and Development*, Number 1, 1982, pp 301-324

Barr A and Feigenbaum E A, *The Handbook of Artificial Intelligence*, Volume 2, Pitman, 1982

Bond A, Change in rules for intelligence, *Computing*, 5 March 1981, pp 18-19

Cole B C, Artificial intelligence and the personal computer user, *Interface Age*, April 1981, pp 88-90

d'Agapeyeff A, *Expert Systems, Fifth Generation and UK Suppliers*, NCC Publications, 1983

Duda R et al, Model design in the PROSPECTOR consultant system for mineral exploration, in D Michie (ed), *Expert Systems in the Microelectronics Age*, Edinburgh University Press, 1980

Fagan L M, *VM: Representing Time Dependent Relations in a Medical Setting*, Dissertation, Computer Science Department, Stanford University, USA, 1980

Hartley R T, CRIB: computer fault-finding through knowledge engineering, *Computer*, March 1984, pp 76-83

Mace S, Expert-Ease creates expert systems on IBM PC, *Infoworld*, 19 March 1984, pp 11-12

Michaelsen R and Michie D, Expert systems in business, *Datamation*, November 1983, pp 240-246

Pratt C A, An artificially intelligent locomotive mechanic, *Simulation*, January 1984, pp 40-41

Roberts F C and Park O, Intelligent computer-assisted instruction: an explanation and overview, *Educational Technology*, December 1983, pp 7-12

Rogers W et al, Computer-aided medical diagnosis: literature review, *International Journal of Biomedical Computing*, 10, 1979, pp 267-289

Sedlmeyer R L et al, Knowledge-based fault localisation in debugging, *The Journal of Systems and Software*, December 1983, pp 301-307

Shaket E, Fuzzy semantics for a natural-like language defined over a world of blocks, *Artificial Intelligence*, Memo 4, University of California, 1976

Stefik M J and de Kleer J, Prospects for expert systems in CAD, *Computer Design*, 21 April 1983, pp 65-76

Thomas D E et al, Automatic data path synthesis, *Computer*, December 1983, pp 59-70

Watt P, Micros become 'experts', *Infoworld*, 23 April 1984, pp 40-41

Webster R, Expert systems, *Personal Computer World*, January 1983, pp 118-119

Zadeh L A, Fuzzy sets, *Information and Control*, 8, 1965, pp 338-353

CHAPTER 9

Agin G J, Computer vision systems for industrial inspection and assembly, *Computer*, May 1980, pp 11-20

Braggins D, Vision systems: helping robots to see things our way . . ., *Machinery and Production Engineering*, 18 April 1984, pp 38-41

Bruno C, Every home should have one . . ., *Infomatics*, January 1984, p 12

Corrado J K, Military-industrial cooperation advances robotics applications, *Mini-Micro Systems*, December 1983, pp 122-124

Creeger M, Lisp machines come out of the lab, *Computer Design*, November 1983, pp 207-216

Davies B L, The use of robots to aid the severely disabled, *Electronics and Power*, March 1984, pp 211-214

Durham T, Lessons that the robot has got to master, *Computing*, 1 March 1984, p 25

Foster E S, Two firms aim LISP AI systems at commercial market, *Mini-Micro Systems*, October 1983, pp 62-68

Garrett R C, A natural approach to artificial intelligence, *Interface Age*, April 1978, pp 80-83

Iversen W R, Military has its eye on speech, *Electronics*, 5 June 1980, pp 93-94

Keller E L, Clever robots set to enter industry en masse, *Electronics*, 17 November 1983, pp 116-129

Manuel T, Lisp and Prolog machines are proliferating, *Electronics*, 3 November 1983, pp 132-137

Melear C, 8-bit μC directs robot controllers, *Electronic Design*, 10 November 1983, pp 177-186

Meyer J D, Commercial machine vision systems, *Computer Graphics World*, October 1983, pp 74-84

Schreiner L, 7-axis robot automates manufacturing work cell, *Electronic Design*, 10 November 1983, pp 141-148

Simons G L, *Towards Fifth-Generation Computers*, NCC Publications, 1983

Togai M, Japan's next generation of robots, *Computer*, March 1984, pp 19-25

Welch, J R, Automatic speech recognition – putting it to work in industry, *Computer*, May 1980, pp 65-73

Witkowski M, Planning techniques find optimal routes, *Practical Computing*, June 1980, pp 90-94

Appendix 2

SELECT BIBLIOGRAPHY

Select Bibliography

Most of these publications are also cited in Appendix 1, but they are worth highlighting as deserving particular attention.

Boden M, *Artificial Intelligence and Natural Man,* Harvester Press, 1977, 537 pp
(*Discusses what AI is, gives detailed descriptions of important AI systems, and discusses the psychological, philosophical and social implications*)

Barr A and Feigenbaum E A, *The Handbook of Artificial Intelligence*, Volume 1, Pitman, 1981, 409 pp
(*Discusses, in conjunction with Volumes 2 and 3, every aspect of AI research. Volume 2 deals with expert systems and other matters. These three volumes are a definitive statement of virtually all the topics of interest to workers in the field. Some of the sections are more accessible than others. Many references are given to papers of importance in the history of AI*)

Barr A and Feigenbaum E A, *The Handbook of Artificial Intelligence*, Volume 2, Pitman, 1982, 428 pp

Cohen P R and Feigenbaum E A, *The Handbook of Artificial Intelligence*, Volume 3, Pitman, 1982, 640 pp

Claxton G (editor), *Cognitive Psychology: New Directions*, Routledge & Kegan Paul, 1980, 338 pp
(*Discusses many of the topics of interest to cognitive psychologists – actions, attention, memory, psycholinguistics, etc. Talks about the relevance of computers and AI in various connections*)

Feigenbaum E A and McCorduck P, *The Fifth Generation: Artificial Intelligence and Japan's Computer Challenge to the World*, Michael Joseph, 1983, 275 pp
(*Provides a useful layperson's guide to artificial intelligence, expert systems and the Japanese plans for fifth-generation computer systems. Sets these topics in a broad international context*)

Hayes J E, Michie D and Pao Y-H (eds), *Machine Intelligence*, 10, Ellis Horwood, John Wiley & Sons (distributors), 1982, 584 pp
(*Surveys new AI developments in computer vision, robotics, logic programming, etc*)

Hofstadter D R, *Gödel, Escher, Bach: An Eternal Golden Braid*, Harvester Press, 1979
(*Termed a 'Metaphorical Fugue on Minds and Machines in the Spirit of Lewis Carroll', this book is worth dipping into. It is a curious, and sometimes ponderous, mix of AI, imaginative dialogues, engaging insights, etc.*)

Lindsay P H and Norman D A, *Human Information Processing: An Introduction to Psychology*, Academic Press, New York, 1977, 777 pp
(*An excellent introduction to the information-processing approach to human psychology. Discusses many topics – eg pattern recognition, memory, knowledge representation – of direct relevance to AI. Accessible text well supported by diagrams*)

Pyle D W, *Intelligence*, Routledge and Kegan Paul, 1979, 123 pp
(*Compact survey of attitudes to, and our knowledge of, intelligence. Discusses nature of intelligence, measurement, relevant causal factors, learning, etc. Includes comprehensive 11-page bibliography*)

Winston P H, *Artificial Intelligence*, Addison-Wesley, 1979 (reprinted in 1984), 444 pp
(*A detailed survey of all the main AI areas. Includes a discussion of expert systems, a section on LISP programming, and 'problems to think about' for Chapters 2 to 16*)

Appendix 3

SOME AI SYSTEMS

Some AI Systems

This list of AI systems is included to indicate the wide-ranging nature of work in this field. This is far from an exhaustive compilation: for instance, there are many AI programs that are not labelled by a convenient acronym or other name, and in any case new programs are being written all the time, many of which will never be cited or described in journals and other publications. This list includes experimental and practical systems of many different levels of competence and complexity. (Experimental and practical expert systems are denoted by e.s.)

ABEL (e.s.) diagnoses acid/base electrolyte disorders.

ABSTRIPS solves problems by developing an appropriate hierarchy to identify epistemologically appropriate levels.

ACRONYM provides artificial vision, deriving three-dimensional information from a monocular image.

ACT models aspects of human memory.

AGE (e.s.) formulates hypotheses to aid the development of expert systems.

AIRPLAN (e.s.) plans air traffic movement around an aircraft carrier.

AL/X (e.s.) aids encoding of knowledge to assist diagnostic experts.

AM discovers concepts in elementary mathematics and set theory.

AQ11 learns to discriminate between training rules.

BACON solves various single-concept learning tasks.

BASEBALL (e.s.) answers questions about stored information on baseball.

BUGGY (e.s.) identifies a student's basic arithmetic misconceptions.

BUILD solves problems by, in part, mimicking commonsense strategies.

CADUCEUS (e.s.) diagnoses conditions in internal medicine.

CALLISTO (e.s.) models, monitors, schedules and manages large projects.

CASNET (e.s.) associates treatments with diagnostic hypotheses, applied to glaucoma.

CHI (e.s.) generates programs using a knowledge base.

CONGEN (e.s.) solves molecular structures.

CRYSALIS (e.s.) analyses protein crystallography data.

DART (e.s.) diagnoses computer system faults, used in field engineering.

DEACON performs inferences on stored knowledge.

DEDALUS (e.s.) transforms program descriptions to aid automatic program generation.

DENDRAL (e.s.) interprets mass spectrometry data to determine molecular structure and atomic constituents.

Digitalis Therapy Advisor (e.s.) advises physicians on use of the drug digitalis.

DIPMETER ADVISOR (e.s.) analyses information from oil well logs.

DRAGON understands spoken words.

DRILLING ADVISOR (e.s.) diagnoses oil well drilling problems, advises on corrective measures.

ELIZA converses with psychiatric patient, not strictly an AI program but much cited.

EMYCIN (e.s.) used in many fields as a basic inference system, based on MYCIN.

EURISKO (e.s.) used to design three-dimensional electronic circuits, learns by discovery.

EXCHECK (e.s.) teaches university-level courses in logic, set theory and proof theory.

EXPERT (e.s.) used in oil exploration and medical applications.

FOO converts high-level advice into effective, executable procedures.

FRUMP summarises textual accounts (news reports, etc).

GENESIS (e.s.) helps to plan and simulate gene-splicing experiments.

GPS (General Problem Solver) solves problems in several different subject areas, successor to the Logic Theorist.

GUIDON (e.s.) teaches students by eliciting and correcting answers to questions.

GUS understands natural language.

HACKER models the process of acquiring programming skills, learns by experience in manipulating simulated blocks.

HAM models aspects of human memory.

HARPY aids document retrieval, understands natural language.

HASP/SIAP (e.s.) identifies and tracks ships by means of ocean sonar signals.

HEADMED (e.s.) advises on psychopharmacology procedures.

HEARSAY-I plays chess, understands natural language.

HEARSAY-II aids document retrieval, understands natural language.

HODGKINS (e.s.) plans diagnostic procedures for Hodgkins disease.

HWIM answers questions by referring to a knowledge base.

HYDRO (e.s.) solves water resource problems.

ID3 learns in various domains, a development of the CLS algorithm; has written chess programs.

IDEOLOGY MACHINE simulates conversational responses of committed ideologues (eg Barry Goldwater).

INTERNIST (e.s.) diagnoses diseases (two versions INTERNIST-I and INTERNIST-II are available).

INTERPLAN solves planning problems.

INTERPRET analyses imperfect line drawings.

IRIS (e.s.) helps physicians to experiment with various consultation systems.

ISIS (e.s.) aids job shop scheduling.

KAS (e.s.) creates, modifies or deletes rule networks to be represented in PROSPECTOR.

KBVLSI (e.s.) aids the development of VLSI designs.

KEPE (e.s.) represents knowledge for various commercial purposes.

KM-I (e.s.) integrates capabilities of data management system and knowledge base system.

KS-300 (e.s.) used for industrial diagnostic and advising applications.

LDS (e.s.) models decision-making processes of lawyers involved in product liability legislation.

LEX solves symbolic integration problems.

LHASA (e.s.) synthesises organic substances.

LIFER interprets English to generate formalised queries for an information retrieval system.

Logic Theorist solves problems, precursor to GPS, one of the first programs to use heuristics in problem-solving.

LOGOS understands continuous spoken speech.

LOOPS (e.s.) used to aid knowledge representation in KBVLSI.

LUNAR (e.s.) answers questions about lunar geology.

MACSYMA (e.s.) solves wide range of mathematical problems to aid scientists, engineers and others.

MARGIE used to memorise, analyse, and make inferences in English.

MEMOD models aspects of human memory (particularly long-term memory).

Meta-DENDRAL (e.s.) used for theory construction (see also DENDRAL).

MOLGEN (e.s.) plans experiments involving analysis and synthesis of DNA.

MRS (e.s.) used to aid knowledge representation and problem solving control, termed a 'Metalevel Representation System'.

MYCIN (e.s.) diagnoses meningitis and blood infections (see also EMYCIN).

MYCROFT assesses and corrects drawings done by computers programmed to draw by children.

NLPQ (e.s.) interprets natural-language dialogue to aid program generation.

NOAH solves various problems.

ONCOCIN (e.s.) used as a protocol management system for cancer chemotherapy treatment.

OPS (e.s.) inference system applicable for many fields, used for RI and AIRPLAN.

PAM understands stories.

PARRY ('paranoid') models behaviour of paranoid human being.

PECOS (e.s.) transforms program descriptions to aid automatic program generation.

PIP (e.s.) diagnoses kidney disease.

POLY interprets line drawings.

POPEYE recognises shapes in line drawings and other visual presentations.

PROGRAMMER'S APPRENTICE (e.s.) assists in software construction and debugging.

PROSPECTOR (e.s.) evaluates geological sites for potential mineral deposits.

Protosystem I generates programs.

PSI (e.s.) generates computer programs from an English description of the required task.

PUFF (e.s.) diagnoses possible lung disorders.

RABBIT (e.s.) helps user to formulate queries to a data base.

RI (e.s.) configures VAX computer systems.

ROSIE (e.s.) inference system applicable to many problems.

RX (e.s.) aids medical diagnosis.

SACON (e.s.) aids the analysis of structural engineering problems.

SAD-SAM answers questions in a limited domain (kinship relations).

SAFE generates a program from a preparsed English specification.

SAGE (e.s.) inference system applicable to many problems.

SAINT solves elementary symbolic integration problems.

SAM understands stories.

Samuel Draughts-Player plays draughts ('checkers'), learns by experience.

SCHOLAR (e.s.) answers geographical questions by extrapolating from its knowledge.

SECS (e.s.) assists chemists in planning organic synthesis.

SEE analyses how many three-dimensional objects are depicted in line drawings.

SHRDLU simulates a conversational robot that can, for example, move blocks in the world.

SIN solves symbolic integration problems.

SIR answers questions in a limited domain.

SOPHIE (e.s.) diagnoses faults in electronic circuits.

SPARC solves learning problems that arise in the card game Eleusis.

SPEAR (e.s.) analyses computer error logs, used in field engineering.

STRIPS solves a wide range of problems, used in the SHAKEY mobile robot designed at SRI.

STUDENT (e.s.) solves algebra problems.

SYNCHEM (e.s.) synthesises organic substances.

TALE-SPIN writes fictional stories.

TATR (e.s.) used for tactical air targeteering, uses ROSIE.

TAXMAN (e.s.) deals with rules implicit in tax laws, suggests contractual arrangements for companies.

TEIRESIAS (e.s.) transfers knowledge from human expert to a system, guides acquisition of new inference rules.

TLC performs inferences on stored knowledge.

TOPLE uses presented knowledge to carry out inferential procedures.

UNITS (e.s.) knowledge representation system used in building MOLGEN and AGE.

VISIONS provides artificial vision.

VM (e.s.) monitors patients in intensive care, advises about respiratory therapy.

WAVES (e.s.) advises engineers on the use of seismic data analysis procedures for oil industry.

WEST (e.s.) teaches students who are enabled to learn by interacting with a coach.

WHISPER reasons by means of analogical representation.

WHY (e.s.) teaches students about rainfall, an extension of SCHOLAR.

WUMPUS (e.s.) teaches logic, probability theory, decision theory and geometry.

XCON (e.s.) configures VAX computer systems (see also XSEL).

XSEL (e.s.) XCON extension to assist salespeople to select computer systems.

INDEX

Index